Woods Practical Guide

to Noise Control

Ian Sharland, B.Sc.(Eng.), C.Eng., A.F.R.Ae.S.

with a foreward by Peter Lord, B.Sc., M.Sc.Tech., Ph.D.,
F.Inst.P., C.Eng., M.I.E.E., Professor of Acoustics, Salford University

Published by
WOODS OF COLCHESTER LIMITED
A member of the GEC group of companies

First published May 1972

Copyright Ian Sharland 1972

MADE AND PRINTED IN ENGLAND BY
WATERLOW AND SONS LTD., LONDON AND DUNSTABLE

Foreword

In recent years a number of books on acoustics have appeared which are aimed at satisfying the requirements of the student and research worker and, as such, are most welcome. In my opinion, however, the expert has been slow to explain the results of his work to the practising engineer who frequently finds himself faced with the problem of controlling noise and yet does not possess the technical background which would enable him to deal with it with any reasonable chance of success.

With the publication of this book, therefore, a conspicuous gap in the literature on acoustics has been filled. Ian Sharland is an expert in the practical application of sound attenuation principles and here, in this guide, he sets out those principles and offers logical and straightforward methods for the control of noise.

It is no simple task to present technical information which is the product of a highly mathematical field in a way which is comprehensible to the non-mathematician. Nevertheless, this book represents a genuine effort to do just this, using as its central theme the measurement and control of noise in ventilating systems.

Other related areas of practical acoustics are also covered but keeping the mathematics to a minimum and making use, wherever possible, of tables and graphical representation. In fact, the reader will find that he needs little more than a modest knowledge of logarithms to be able to read and understand the whole book.

PETER LORD

Salford, March 1972

Author's Preface

To speak of the subject of "Acoustics" nowadays is rather like speaking of "Engineering" or "Economics". The words describe fields of study rather than specific topics. Acoustics has grown far beyond the still widely-held association with the third part of the old "Heat, Light and Sound" courses, and its range now includes such diversified disciplines as medicine and social psychology, through to solid-state physics and mathematical statistics. Somewhere in between lies a comparatively new and rapidly-growing technology, which is coming to be known as noise control engineering.

The number of professional noise control engineers is still small, but an increasing number of practitioners in the more established fields of mechanical, electrical, heating and ventilating, and process engineering are finding themselves faced with the need to know more about noise control. Not only engineers, but also architects, town planners, public health inspectors, factory inspectors, and industrial safety officers will at some time have asked, or have been asked the question "How can we make it less noisy?"

First reactions may be to call in the professional acoustician, and it must be said that in many cases this is undoubtedly the best action. On the other hand, there are a whole range of everyday noise problems which could easily be overcome with a good grounding in the principles, procedures and codes of practice which invariably have to be invoked, even by the experts. With such knowledge the engineer, architect or inspector, faced with noise, can certainly cope with the more straightforward problems and, even if he has to consult the expert, it would enable him to follow the reasoning behind the eventual recommendations.

It is the object of this book to provide the core of knowledge which is so essential. It is not the last word on acoustics—rather it is intended to be a first word for those to whom noise control is a new field.

The starting point, as with any new study, is with fundamentals—how noise occurs, its structure, and the units and definitions used to describe it. Then follows an examination of why it is that noise needs to be controlled at all, its effect upon people, and the limits which should be placed upon it. After a short chapter on how acoustical parameters are measured in the laboratory, the book deals with what to many people is the most difficult part of any investigation: how to estimate the amount of noise which is likely to occur in a given situation. A special chapter is devoted to the acoustic assessment of ventilating and air conditioning systems. The final chapters cover techniques of noise control: first outlining the general

Author's Preface

principles upon which almost all noise control measures are based, and then how to put these principles into practice. Whenever appropriate, the text is illustrated by practical worked examples.

Throughout the book, the intention has been to emphasise the physical reasons for the choice of criteria, for the mathematical formulae involved, and for the methods of reducing noise.

In a work of this kind only the presentation and certain subject matter related to one's own experience can claim to be original. For the bulk of the subject matter, I am indebted to all my associates and colleagues in the field of acoustics, who directly and indirectly have over the years passed their knowledge on to me. If I have not detailed every reference from which material is drawn, it is because that material is firmly established as authoritative in the field, and its author is widely recognised. I am especially grateful to Malcolm Meredith, Managing Director of Woods of Colchester, without whose support, constant encouragement and inexhaustible patience, the book would not have been produced at all. I would like to thank Peter Lord for his helpful and constructive criticism of the technical matter, and my colleagues at Woods who have spent many hours in proof-reading, correcting, editing and generally keeping me under control.

IAN SHARLAND

March 1972

Contents

Contents

Contents

Symbols and abbreviations used in the text

A	Total absorption (m² units)
c	Velocity of sound
D	Sound energy density
DI	Directivity index
DRC	Damage risk criterion
dB	Decibel
dBA	Decibel measured with standard "A" scale weighting
dBB	Decibel measured with standard "B" scale weighting
dBC	Decibel measured with standard "C" scale weighting
E	Modulus of elasticity
f	Frequency
H_e	Hertz (cycles per second)
h_e	Effective barrier height
I	Sound intensity (rate of energy flow through unit area)
IL	Insertion loss
k	Constant
M	Surface density
NC	Noise criterion
NR	Noise rating
p	Fan static pressure
p_{ref}	Reference sound pressure $(2 \times 10^{-5} \text{ N/m}^2)$
Q	Volume flow
Q_θ	Directivity factor
R	Sound reduction index
R_c	Room constant
R_f	Flow resistance
S	Area
SIL	Speech interference level
SPL	Sound pressure level
SWL	Sound power level
T	Reverberation time
V	Volume
W	Sound power
W_{ref}	Reference sound power (10^{-12} watt)
α	Absorption coefficient
$\bar{\alpha}$	Average absorption coefficient
δ	Static deflection
θ	Angular direction
λ	Wavelength
ϱ	Density
τ	Transmission coefficient
ω	Angular frequency $(2\pi f)$

Index to figures and tables

Index to figures and tables

CHAPTER 1

Some fundamental concepts

Physical structure of waves

For a full understanding of how to control noise, it is essential to have a knowledge of the physical nature of sound and the way it behaves.

We might start by reflecting why it is that noise needs to be controlled at all. Almost without exception it is because someone is being subjected to a sound pressure level which is too high. We shall define precisely what is meant by sound pressure level later—for the moment, we need just to accept that when we say sound pressure level is too high, we are really saying that variations in air pressure near his ear are of too high an amplitude. This is perhaps the first fundamental point to grasp—what we usually call sound is a variation of pressure in the region of air adjacent to the ear. We have to qualify this of course, and distinguish between acoustic changes and meteorological changes. We shall see later how fundamental the differences are. For the moment it will suffice to say that the magnitude of acoustic pressure fluctuations are many times less than normal atmospheric pressure variations, and occur many times more rapidly. Having realised then that what we are really concerned with is nothing more than an alternating pressure in a small volume of air, the next logical question is how does it happen? What causes the pressure in this elemental volume to alternate? The answer is simple. It happens because a very short, but finite, time before, exactly the same pattern of pressure variation took place in the elemental volume which was immediately next to the first one. And, a short time before that, the process occurred in the next volume element in line—and so on right back to the "source" of sound.

How does the source initiate these disturbances in the first place? This is best explained in terms of a very simple model of a sound source. Consider a long tube filled with air and fitted at one end with a piston (fig. 1.1). Now let us move the piston forward a short distance. The first thing that we realise of course is that the air in the tube does not move forward like a solid plug. Because the air is elastic, only the molecules immediately next to the face of the piston move at first. In other words, the pressure in the element of air next to the piston increases. If we hold the piston in this position for a moment, the element of air under compression obviously tries to expand. It cannot expand backwards or sideways because both piston face and tube walls are rigid. So it expands forward along the tube. When we say expand, we mean that the individual molecules move forward, and in doing so they displace the next layer of

1

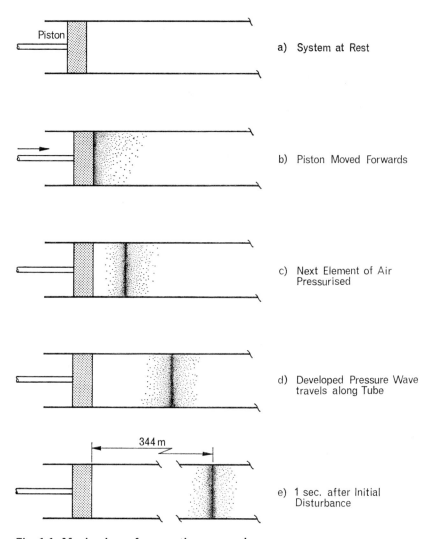

Fig. 1.1. Mechanism of generating a sound wave

molecules. That is, they compress the next elemental volume of air. The process is then repeated, so that the next element again becomes compressed and so on. The net result being that a "wave" of positive pressure is transmitted down the tube.

If we now move the piston in the opposite direction the positive pressure in the original volume element starts to decrease, and eventually, when the piston passes its mid position, it goes negative. By the reverse process then, a wave of negative pressure follows in the wake of the original positive pressure wave.

As a side comment here, it should be noted that when we refer to "positive" and "negative" pressures, we mean above or below the static pressure of the air at rest in the tube.

We can then, generate a positive pressure wave or a negative pressure wave. But we still have not generated sound. In fact if a single wave reached our ear, we probably would not call it sound at all, but rather describe it as a "thud" or a "click", depending upon the shape of the wave. Sound, as we shall be dealing with throughout this book, is in fact a continuous succession of waves. All we need to do then with our model, is to move the piston alternately forwards and backwards continuously, and we are generating not just a series of individual compressions and rarefractions, but sound.

The velocity of sound

One thing that will be immediately obvious from this explanation of the process of generating a wave, is that it takes a definite time after the piston has moved, to compress the air in the second elemental volume, and a longer time still to compress the air in the third elemental volume. In fact, if the air was at 20°C it would take one second to compress the air in an element 344 metres down the tube—which of course defines the "velocity of sound" (normally denoted by c) in air at 20°C.

Although we have been confining our example to a wave moving in air, it is important to realise that the same process can take place in any medium that has elasticity—which includes virtually all liquids and gases, and most solids too. Certainly common building materials like concrete,

TABLE 1.1

Velocity of sound in various materials

Material	Approximate velocity of sound m/sec
Air	344
Lead	1220
Water	1410
Brick	3000
Wood	3400
Concrete	3400
Glass	4100
Aluminium	5100
Steel	5200

masonry, timber, steel and glass, can all carry sound waves, some of them quite well. In fact, it is their ability to do so which presents some of the most difficult problems, as we shall see later. One way in which the propagation of sound waves in these other materials differs from that in air, is the velocity at which the waves travel. The important parameters which determine the velocity of sound in a material are its modulus of elasticity, E, and its density, ρ. It can be shown in fact that

$$\text{velocity of sound} = k \sqrt{\frac{E}{\varrho}} \qquad (1.1)$$

Consequently sound travels faster in materials having high elasticity, and low density. Table 1.1 shows the value for some common materials.

Wavelength and Frequency

To return to our air-filled tube. Quite apart from the speed of the waves, we will have noticed something else. With a regular cyclic motion of the piston in each direction, as shown in fig. 1.2, successive high pressure waves are regularly spaced apart, as also of course are successive low pressure ones. The distance between successive waves of the same sense is called the "wave-length" of sound in the medium and is usually denoted by λ.

Another fundamental parameter which describes a sound is its frequency (normally denoted f)—that is, the number of like waves which pass by a fixed observation point per second. Obviously, since each forward movement of our piston produced a wave of positive pressure, frequency is also the number of complete cycles of the piston movement per second. The unit of frequency is the Hertz, abbreviated Hz.

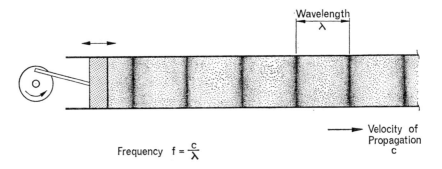

Fig. 1.2. Generation of continuous sound

If we examine again the situation of a succession of sound waves moving through the medium, it is clear that frequency, wavelength, and velocity of propagation, are all related. Quite simply,

wavelength × number of wavelengths passing per unit time (frequency)
= velocity

or, to use the usual notation,

$$\lambda \times f = c \qquad (1.2)$$

This means that if we know the speed of sound in a medium, we can calculate the wavelength of a sound at any particular frequency. Since the behaviour of sound is usually dependent upon its wavelength, as we shall see later, this relationship is important.

Sound intensity and power

We have now arrived at the point where we recognise sound as a succession of travelling pressure waves moving away from the source (in our model, the piston). Simply because they are travelling, they must be transmitting something. When we say that pressure is being transmitted, it is the same thing of course as saying that force is being transmitted, and since the force is moving, there must be a nett flow of momentum and hence energy. So we arrive at a very important conclusion that sound waves transmit energy.

In a sound field consisting of waves emanating from a source it is usual to refer to the "intensity" of sound at a point. Intensity (usually denoted I) is the amount of energy passing through unit area per unit time and is expressed for example in watts/m². There is a direct relationship between intensity and acoustic pressure; intensity being directly proportional to the square of the pressure. This means that since sound-measuring instruments measure pressure directly, we can always express this as a value of intensity. From there it is a relatively straightforward matter to calculate the *total* acoustic power produced by the source, as we shall now see.

Let us take our piston from the end of the tube and suspend it with some means of oscillating it (in fact an unbaffled loudspeaker would serve very well) in the centre of a very large volume of air, which is completely free of reflecting surfaces (fig. 1.3). When the piston is oscillated now, sound waves will spread spherically from it. This is because the element of air first compressed by the movement of the piston face, can spread sideways as well. Assume it spreads equally in all directions. Now let us enclose the source with an imaginary control surface which we will make a sphere of radius r. Let us say that the sound pressure at any point on a spherical wave travelling through the control surface is p. Then we can show that the acoustic intensity at any point on the surface is given by

$$I = p^2/\varrho c \qquad (1.3)$$

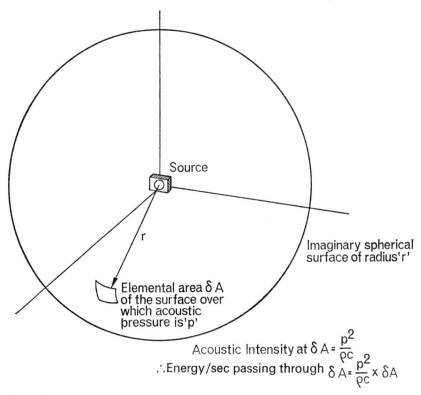

Acoustic Intensity at $\delta A = \dfrac{p^2}{\rho c}$

$\therefore$ Energy/sec passing through $\delta A = \dfrac{p^2}{\rho c} \times \delta A$

Fig. 1.3. Sound pressure and sound energy

Here, ρ is the density of the medium, and c is the velocity of sound in it. The product ρc is known as the "acoustic impedance" of the medium, and immediately one may see an analogy with electrical theory viz.

$$\text{power} = \frac{(\text{voltage})^2}{\text{resistance}}$$

Now if we consider an elemental area δA on our control surface, we know at once that, by definition of intensity, the total energy passing through it per second is

$$\delta w = \text{intensity} \times \delta A$$

$$= \frac{p^2}{\rho c} \times \delta A \tag{1.4}$$

To get the power passing through all such elemental areas, that is the total power generated by the source, we simply have to integrate over the spherical surface.

i.e. total power = sum of all values of $[p^2/\rho c]\, \delta A$ on the surface (1.5)

$$\text{total power} = \frac{p^2}{\rho c} \cdot 4\pi r^2 \tag{1.6}$$

The final result here was a simple one because we stipulated that the radiation should be equal in all directions, so that p was constant at all points on the surface area.

Not all sources radiate sound in such a manner however. Some exhibit quite strong directional effects, but the same method of assessing the total power output will apply. The variation of p^2 in equation (1.5), has to be determined first, either by measurement or calculation and then the integration follows.

The same principle would in fact have applied to our piston-in-tube model. If at some point well along the tube we had determined the average sound pressure, p, then the intensity at that point would be, as before (equation (1.3)).

$$I = p^2/\varrho c$$

and the total power would be

$$W = \frac{p^2}{\varrho c} \times \text{cross-sectional area of tube} \tag{1.7}$$

Units

We have so far talked of our sound waves only in terms of their general structure, and referred to their magnitude rather loosely in terms of "pressure". Pressure is a perfectly good engineering unit, so if we want a measure of the quantity of sound why not measure the pressure amplitude of the wave? We could do this quite well in fact, but unfortunately a linear measure of pressure does not correspond very well to how the ear reacts.

In the first place, the ear responds to intensity. That is, as we have seen, it detects pressure squared rather than pressure. But, even if we used a linear scale based on p^2, we should still be in trouble, because of the remarkable sensitivity of the ear. The lowest sound intensity that the normal ear can detect is about 10^{-12} watts/m². At the opposite end of the scale, the highest intensity that the normal ear can withstand without feeling physical pain is about 10 watts/m². In other words, if we were to use a linear scale of (pressure)², we would need to allot 10^{13} unit divisions to it to cover the range of human experience.

But this is clearly an unmanageable scale, and it must be compressed. Fortunately, another peculiarity of the hearing mechanism aids our choice. The response of the ear to changes of intensity is more logarithmic than linear. So we will be getting nearer to a unit representing what we actually hear if, instead of (pressure)², we say that the sound has an amplitude of $\log_{10}$ (pressure)².

A start, but still not in its most convenient form. Quite apart from the possibility of negative units (if (pressure)² is numerically less than unity), the value of (pressure)^2 becomes much more meaningful if we can relate it to some common experience, or datum level—in other words, if we express it as a ratio of some constant reference (pressure)^2. In fact, this is just what we do, and the reference we use is the pressure corresponding to the lowest intensity the ear can normally detect, which is 2×10^{-5} N/m^2. We could then say that our unit of sound was

$$\log{._{10}} \frac{(\text{pressure})^2}{(2 \times 10^{-5})^2}$$

Electrical engineers will recognise this at once as a "Bel"—a unit which gives the number of tenfold changes between two quantities. Unfortunately the Bel compresses our scale rather too much—there now being only thirteen divisions between the threshold of hearing and the threshold of pain. So in acoustical engineering we divide the Bel into ten, and work with decibels, abbreviated dB. Now we finally have a unit of sound which is both manageable and gives us some representation of aural response, i.e.

$$\text{Sound Pressure Level} = 10 \log{._{10}} \frac{(\text{sound pressure})^2}{(\text{reference pressure})^2} \text{ dB} \quad (1.8)$$

Where reference pressure $= 2 \times 10^{-5}$ N/m^2.

Sound pressure level is usually abbreviated SPL. We can do exactly the same thing for sound power and define a corresponding unit, i.e.

$$\text{Sound Power Level} = 10 \log_{10} \frac{(\text{sound power})}{(\text{reference power})} \text{ dB} \quad (1.9)$$

Where reference power $= 10^{-12}$ watts.

Sound power level is usually abbreviated SWL although on occasion PWL is used. (Because logarithms to the base 10 are almost invariably used in acoustics, it is not necessary to always write the suffix "10". In the rest of this and following chapters, the suffix is omitted on the understanding that "10" is always implied unless stated.)

EXAMPLE 1.1

In a test to measure the sound power level of an unbaffled loud speaker, it was found that the sound pressure everywhere on the surface of an imaginary sphere of radius 3 metres, centred at the loudspeaker, was 0·2 N/m^2. Calculate the sound pressure level at 3 metres, and the sound power level of the source.

From equation (1.8),
$$\text{SPL} = 10 \log \frac{(2 \times 10^{-1})^2}{(2 \times 10^{-5})^2}$$
$$= 10 \log 10^8$$
$$= 80 \text{ dB}$$

From equation (1.6), total power $= \dfrac{p^2}{\varrho c} \cdot 4\pi r^2$

$$= \frac{(2 \times 10^{-1})^2}{1.18 \times 344} \cdot 4\pi(3)^2 \ \text{Nm/sec}$$

$$= \cdot 0115 \ \text{Watts}$$

From equation (1.9), $\quad$ SWL $= 10 \log \dfrac{1.15 \times 10^{-2}}{10^{-12}}$

$$= 100.6 \ \text{dB}$$

Besides telling us the magnitude of sound pressure or sound power in relation to a reference quantity of common experience, these units also tell us by how much the pressure or power changes.

EXAMPLE 1.2

(a) Calculate the change in sound pressure level if the sound pressure is doubled.

(b) Calculate the change in sound power level if the sound power is doubled.

(a) Let SPL_1 be the sound pressure level corresponding to sound pressure p and SPL_2 be the sound pressure level corresponding to sound pressure $2p$.

Then $SPL_1 = 10 \log \dfrac{p^2}{p_{\text{ref}}^2}$

$$SPL_2 = 10 \log \frac{4p^2}{p_{\text{ref}}^2} = 10 \log \frac{p^2}{p_{\text{ref}}^2} + 10 \log 4$$

$$= SPL_1 + 6 \ \text{dB}$$

(b) Let SWL_1 be the sound power level corresponding to sound power W and SWL_2 be the sound power level corresponding to sound power 2W.

Then $SWL_1 = 10 \log \dfrac{\text{W}}{\text{W}_{\text{ref}}}$

$$SWL_2 = 10 \log \frac{2\text{W}}{\text{W}_{\text{ref}}} = 10 \log \frac{\text{W}}{\text{W}_{\text{ref}}} + 10 \log 2$$

$$= SWL_1 + 3 \ \text{dB}$$

Hence doubling sound pressure increases the original sound pressure level by 6 dB. Doubling sound power on the other hand increases the original sound power level by only 3dB. We must therefore be careful when we talk about doubling the sound, and define whether we mean pressure or power. One very important point that should be made is that when two sound sources are operating at once, the level of the combined sound is not the arithmetic addition of the individual levels of each source. Rather, it is the level corresponding to the arithmetic addition of the individual *intensities*.

EXAMPLE 1.3

Two sound sources are operating together. One produces a sound pressure level of 74 dB when operating by itself, the other produces a sound pressure level of 70 dB when operating by itself. Calculate the sound pressure level due to both operating together.

Let $SPL_1 = 10 \log \dfrac{p_1^2}{p_{ref}^2} = 74$

then $\qquad\qquad \dfrac{p_1^2}{p_{ref}^2} = 10^{7.4}$

$\qquad\qquad\qquad = 10^7 \times 2 \cdot 51$

Let $SPL_2 = 10 \log \dfrac{p_2^2}{p_{ref}^2} = 70$

then $\qquad\qquad \dfrac{p_2^2}{p_{ref}^2} = 10^7$

Total sound pressure level $= 10 \log \dfrac{(p_1^2 + p_2^2)}{p_{ref}^2}$

$\qquad\qquad = 10 \log (2 \cdot 51 \times 10^7 + 10^7)$

$\qquad\qquad = 10 \log (3 \cdot 51 \times 10^7)$

$\qquad\qquad = 75 \cdot 4 \text{ dB}$

Fortunately we do not have to go through this exercise each time we want to add two sound levels together (the same procedure applies to the addition of sound power levels), we can refer to a simple table as shown in Table 1.2.

Having now defined the decibel for both sound pressure and sound power, let us see what sort of levels are commonly experienced. Table 1.3 shows typical sound pressure levels produced by some everyday sources, and Table 1.4 shows typical sound power levels.

Note in these tables that sound pressure level is always specified at some position—either a stated distance from a source, or in a defined environment. The reason for this, as we shall see later, is that the sound pressure produced by a source of given power is dependent upon both location and distance from the source. On the other hand, the amount of sound power produced and hence the sound power level, is generally independent of the environment in which the source is located. It is therefore always important, when stating a sound pressure level, to qualify it by stating the location also.

TABLE 1.2

Addition of sound levels

Difference between the two levels dB	Add to higher level dB
0	3
1	2·5
2	2
3	2
4	1·5
5	1
6	1
7	1
8	·5
9	·5
10 or more	0

TABLE 1.3

Average sound pressure levels to be expected in some common environments

Sound pressure N/m^2	Sound pressure level dB	Typical environment	Average subjective description
200	140	30 m from military aircraft at take-off	
63	130	Pneumatic chipping and riveting (operator's position)	Intolerable
20	120	Boiler shop (maximum levels) Ships engine room (full speed)	
6·3	110	Automatic punch press (operator's position) Sheet metal shop—hand grinding Textile weaving room	
2	100	Automatic lathe shop Platform of underground station (maximum levels) Printing press room	Very noisy
$6·3 \times 10^{-1}$	90	Heavy lorries at 6 m Construction site—pneumatic drilling	
2×10^{-1}	80	Kerbside of busy street Office with tabulating machines	
$6·3 \times 10^{-2}$	70	Loud radio (in average domestic room)	Noisy
2×10^{-2}	60	Restaurant Department Store	
$6·3 \times 10^{-3}$	50	Conversational speech at 1 m General office	
2×10^{-3}	40	Average suburban area Whispered conversation at 2 m Residential area at night	Quiet
$6·3 \times 10^{-4}$	30		
2×10^{-4}	20	Background in TV and recording studios	Very quiet
$6·3 \times 10^{-5}$	10		
2×10^{-5}	0	Normal threshold of hearing	

TABLE 1.4

Acoustic power of some common sources

Power (watts)	Sound power level dB	Source
25 to 40 million	195	Saturn rocket
100,000	170	Ram jet
		Turbo jet engine with after burner
10,000	160	Turbo jet engine 3200 kg thrust
1,000	150	
		4 propeller airliner
100	140	
10	130	75 piece orchestra ⎱ Peak RMS levels in ⅛ second
		Pipe Organ ⎰ intervals
		Small aircraft engine
1	120	Large chipping hammer
		Piano ⎱ Peak RMS levels in 4 second intervals
		B-flat Tuba ⎰
0·1	110	Blaring radio
		Centrifugal ventilating fan (22,000 m³/h)
0·01	100	1 m Loom
		Car on motorway
0·001	90	Vaneaxial ventilating fan (2500 m³/h)
		Voice—shouting (average long time RMS)
0·0001	80	
0·00001	70	Voice—conversational level (average long time RMS)
0·000001	60	
0·0000001	50	
0·000,000,01	40	
0·000,000,001	30	Voice—very soft whisper

The frequency spectrum

When we were discussing the motion of the piston in our model source, the only stipulation we made was that it had to perform a succession of complete cycles of movement to produce a succession of waves at regular intervals. Its motion had to be periodic in fact. We laid no conditions however, on the manner in which it should move between its extreme positions. We could for example have moved it to its extreme forward position very rapidly, held it there for a short period, moved it quickly to its extreme backward position, held it there, and then repeated the process. If we had then measured, at some point along the tube, the variation of sound pressure with time, using a microphone, we would have found that the sound consisted of a series of rather sharp fronted waves, probably of the form shown in fig. 1.4 (a). By choosing a smoother path between the extreme points we could have produced the more rounded form of waves shown in fig. 1.4 (b).

Now, although both of these waves were produced in the same period of time, that is to say they have the same frequency, they will in fact sound quite different to the ear. The reason for this is that they have quite different "harmonic" content. To explain this, let us examine what

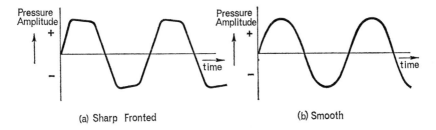

(a) Sharp Fronted   (b) Smooth

Fig. 1.4. Typical waveforms

happens when the piston is moved in the simplest, or rather the mathematically "purest", way possible. We could achieve this by operating the piston by a flywheel (rather like the piston in a car engine), as shown in fig. 1.2.

For a constant flywheel speed, the motion of the piston will of course be simple harmonic. Its position x from the mid position at any time t will be given by

$$x = X \sin \omega t$$

where X is the maximum displacement in either direction
and ω is the angular frequency $= 2\pi f$

We would then find that the instantaneous sound pressure at some point along the tube varied in the same manner as successive waves passed by. That is to say, we could describe the sound pressure p by

$$p = P \sin \omega t$$

where P is the maximum amplitude of the sound wave.

In fact, if we connected the microphone to an oscilloscope we would see a wave form rather like the one shown in the left hand diagram of fig. 1.5 (a). Moreover, had we calibrated the oscilloscope graticule to show us the amplitude, and the periodic time, T ($= 1/f$), then this picture would tell us all we need to know about that particular sound.

There is however an easier way to represent it. Let us look at the right hand diagram of fig. 1.5 (a), which is a plot of sound intensity against frequency. The frequency of the wave we are studying is very easy to identify—because it is a pure sine wave, it has only one frequency which we will call f_0, and it is equal to $1/T$. The representation of this wave on the frequency spectrum (as it is termed) would be simply a straight vertical line of amplitude P^2, positioned at f_0 on the frequency scale. Now we have as much information as the picture of the actual wave gave us.

Suppose we had made the piston move in a more complicated fashion and produced the wave form shown in fig. 1.5 (b). At first sight there seems very little to tell us what sort of sound this is. We can see that it has the same basic frequency (or rather, period) as our original sine wave, but what about the amplitude? Do we take the maximum value, or something rather less to account for the "valleys" in the wave? The answer is that we first have to express the actual wave as a sum of sine waves of different frequencies. This we can do quite easily by carrying out a Fourier analysis on the parent wave, and this example is found to have three components which are

$$P \sin \omega_0 t; \; 0 \cdot 1 \; P \sin 2 \; \omega_0 t; \; 0 \cdot 5 \; P \sin 3\omega_0 t$$

where $\omega_0 = 2 \pi f_0$

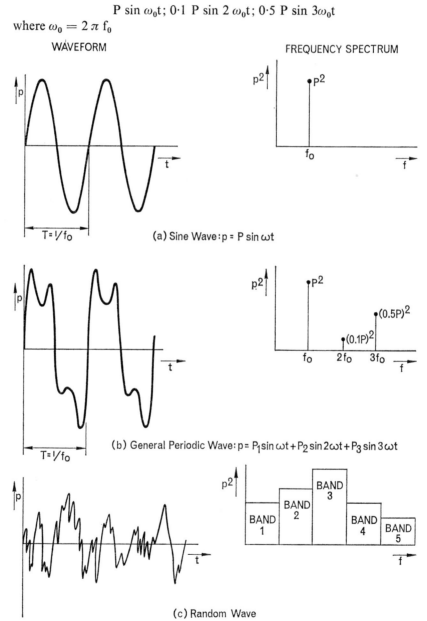

Fig. 1.5. Examples of frequency analysis

Turning then to the frequency spectrum on the right, all we need to represent the wave are three vertical lines at f_0, $2f_0$, and $3f_0$, of amplitude respectively P^2, $(0\cdot1\ P)^2$, and $(0\cdot5\ P)^2$. This tells us far more about the noise than the actual waveform. It tells us for example that the sound will be like listening to three separate sine waves (or "pure tones" as they are termed) at each of the three frequencies, all played together.

We could go on making our waveform more and more complicated and produce some which were constructed of an infinite series of sine waves, but the principle of representing the waveform by its frequency content would be the same. In fact, we would not even need to perform a mathematical analysis to get the frequency spectrum. There are available now, electronic analysers which enable each frequency component to be measured directly.

One thing that all these periodic waves have in common is that however complicated the waveform may be, the fact that they are periodic means that their harmonic components all appear at integral multiples of the fundamental frequency. Unfortunately, the sounds we hear in everyday industrial life are not generally like that. Some sounds it is true, have very pronounced single frequency components which usually contain harmonics, and all we have said so far will apply to those components. What is more usually the case however, is that the waveform of sound pressure against time is very disordered and random in nature, as shown for example in fig. 1.5 (c).

Such a wave has no obvious periodic component, so we cannot think now in terms of a fundamental frequency and a series of ordered harmonics. However, a type of Fourier analysis can be applied to this type of wave and when we do this, we find the perhaps not surprising result that the wave has a component of pressure at *every* frequency. If we were then to attempt to plot the frequency spectrum as before, we would have to draw our vertical lines spaced an infinitesimal distance apart—clearly an impossible task.

For a random type of wave then we plot not the intensity at each and every frequency, but rather the total intensity in a band of frequencies, as shown in the frequency spectrum of fig. 1.5 (c). Again there are a number of instruments available which will enable us to measure with the aid of a microphone precisely how much energy (p^2) lies within a chosen frequency band. The only thing we have to do is to decide which frequency bands we want to use. If we are trying to compare one sound with another, or trying to assess reaction to a noise, things would obviously be much easier if everyone used the same bands. The International Standard Organisation have agreed on "preferred" frequency bands for sound measurement and analysis, and most modern instruments now use them.

The widest band used for frequency analysis is the octave band. That is, the upper frequency limit of the band is exactly twice the lower one. Each octave band is described by its "center frequency" which is the geometric

TABLE 1.5
Preferred frequency bands

Octave band centre frequency Hz	Band limits Hz	One-third octave centre frequency Hz	Band limits Hz
	22		22
31·5		25	
			28
		31·5	
			35
		40	
	44		44
63		50	
			57
		63	
			71
		80	
	88		88
125		100	
			113
		125	
			141
		160	
	176		176
250		200	
			225
		250	
			283
		315	
	353		353
500		400	
			440
		500	
			565
		630	
	707		707
1000		800	
			880
		1000	
			1130
		1250	
	1414		1414
2000		1600	
			1760
		2000	
			2250
		2500	
	2825		2825
4000		3150	
			3530
		4000	
			4400
		5000	
	5650		5650
8000		6300	
			7070
		8000	
			8800
		10000	
	11300		11300
16000		12500	
			14140
		16000	
			17600
		20000	
	22500		22500

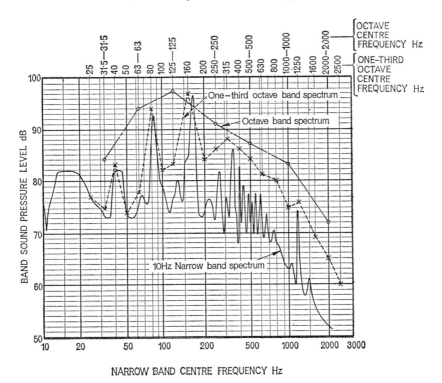

Fig. 1.6. Comparative frequency spectra of noise from a ball mill

mean of the upper and lower frequency limits. The preferred octave bands are shown in terms of their centre frequencies, in Table 1·5.

Occasionally we want a little more information than the octave band will provide on the detailed structure of the noise. This can be obtained by selecting narrower bands, for example one-third octave bands. As the name suggests these are bands of frequency which are a third of the width of an octave band. Again there are preferred frequencies, and they are shown in Table 1·5.

For more scientific examination of the frequency structure of a noise, it is usual to carry out what is known as a "narrow band" analysis. This is a frequency spectrum in which the intensity level plotted at any frequency is the total in a band which may be as little as plus or minus $1\frac{1}{2}$ Hz either side of the centre frequency. Figure 1.6 shows the noise from a ball mill presented as a 10 Hz bandwidth frequency spectrum. Also shown for comparison are the octave, and one-third octave band frequency spectra of the same noise.

CHAPTER 2

Hearing and noise acceptability

The need for criteria

Now that we have gained from the previous chapter some idea of what sound is, and how it can be described, we can proceed to what is one of the first tasks in any noise control exercise—the assessment of just how much noise can be allowed in any given set of circumstances. One might be forgiven for thinking that the simplest answer is to have no noise at all. A point of view certainly, but it could often mean that large sums of money were wasted on bringing a noise level down to less than what would in fact be perfectly acceptable in the particular circumstances.

Noise control does not mean reducing everything to absolute silence. Even if that were possible it would certainly not be desirable—absolute silence can be a most alarming experience. Rather, it means a regulation of the amount of sound energy that reaches an observer to a level which satisfies certain requirements for the environment in which he is placed.

Why is the environment important? We can see the reason if we consider some of the more important ways in which noise can affect people. It can damage hearing, it can interfere with speech communication, it can upset concentration and thereby cause a drop in efficiency, and it can annoy. In a foundry or a sheet metal shop we would not expect to find that the operators were annoyed by the noise resulting from their own work. There may not even be a need there for conversation. But there is a definite need to protect them from hearing damage. For the foundry therefore, our objective is to reduce noise levels to the appropriate damage risk criterion.

In an office or commercial environment on the other hand, not only is there the same fundamental requirement to protect hearing, but also speech communication, particularly telephone conversation, is of prime importance—as may be a good deal of concentration. Thus the requirements here for an acceptable noise level are much more stringent than in a factory environment, and we would have to reduce the noise levels to at least one or other of the speech communication criteria.

Even more stringent are the conditions imposed by the domestic residential environment. Here, it is not sufficient to say that a noise does not cause damage, or does not interfere with concentration. People enjoying the privacy of their homes are entitled to be free from intrusion of noise which may cause them annoyance. This does not necessarily mean that homes must be free of all noise—as we shall see later in this chapter (it depends for one thing on where the homes are) but it does mean that

18

noise levels in residential communities must be carefully controlled. In fact, we have to achieve levels which meet one or other of the residential acceptability criteria.

The most demanding criteria of all are those imposed by special environments like recording and television studios, and some clinical and research facilities. Frequently the nature of the work carried on in such surroundings demands an ambient level approaching the threshold of normal hearing.

By way of summary then, we may compose a "rank order" of severity of criteria for different environments, as shown in Table 2.1.

TABLE 2.1

Order of severity of criteria for the occupants of various environments

Environment	*Requirement*	*Type of noise criterion determining acceptable level*
Industrial fabrication and production shops. Engine, boiler and other plant rooms.	Protection from hearing damage. Little or no speech communication.	Damage risk.
Light industrial assembly or process areas. Business machine areas. Shopping precincts. Commercial kitchens.	Frequent speech communication necessary. Sometimes audio signals used.	Speech interference.
General commercial offices Drawing offices. Restaurants.	Speech communication continuous. Some concentration required.	Speech interference. General acceptability.
Executive offices, Hospitals Hotels, Domestic apartments.	Mental concentration, very important. Private discussions. Rest and comfort.	Comfort. Annoyance.
Theatre auditoria, T.V. and recording studios. Diagnostic clinics. Audiometry rooms. Experimental acoustic laboratories.	Virtual absence of any noise likely to interfere with subject sound.	Minimum background. Threshold of hearing.

The importance of the environment is hence that it determines which type of criterion we should be aiming for—target levels in fact. In this chapter we examine what these criteria are, and how they may be selected to suit given environmental circumstances.

It is easier to grasp the significance of what have become accepted criteria for noise if we first gain an understanding of the mechanism of hearing, and some of its peculiarities.

The hearing mechanism

Figure 2.1 shows a sketch of the basic components of the hearing mechanism.

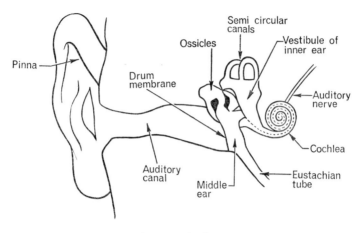

a) Anatomical sketch

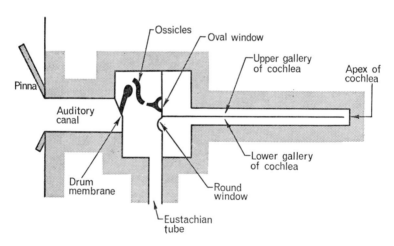

b) Schematic representation

Fig. 2.1. The hearing mechanism

The arrival of sound waves at the ear sets up a fluctuating pressure in the element of air just outside the entrance to the external auditory canal. These pressure fluctuations are then transmitted as pressure waves along the auditory canal—rather like the waves in our earlier model of an air filled tube (fig. 1.2). At the end of the canal is a diaphragm-like membrane known as the tympanic membrane, or eardrum. Being normally under slight tension, the eardrum is physically moved by the action of the sound waves impinging upon it.

On the other side of the eardrum and attached to it, is a linkage of three tiny bones called ossicles, which serve to transmit the motion of the eardrum across the middle ear cavity to another membrane called the oval window. This forms the end of a spiral fluid-filled tube, the cochlea, which is divided into two compartments by a membrane which runs the whole length of the tube, except for a small gap at the end. This membrane carries along its length a complex arrangement of hair cells known as the organ of Corti.

When the oval window is vibrated by the motion of the eardrum, via the ossicles, the fluid in the cochlea is also vibrated. This in turn sets up motion in the membrane and the hair cells. Precisely how the motion of the cells is transformed via the auditory nerve to give a sense of hearing is still not established, but it is known that different regions of the membrane are excited by different frequencies of vibration of the fluid, and it is this which gives us our sense of pitch. The ear in fact has a built-in frequency analyser.

Damage

Quite apart from the possibility of damage from natural causes like disease, the hearing mechanism can suffer from exposure to too much noise. It is therefore of some importance that, as noise control engineers, we are aware of the levels of noise at which this happens. First let us examine what noise-induced hearing loss means.

Contrary to popular belief, hearing loss arising from too much noise is not the result of a "burst" eardrum. This rarely happens, and even when it does, it is usually the result of a pressure type wave, typical of an explosion, and having a peak amplitude of probably 160–180 dB.

In nearly all cases the damage occurs to the delicate hair cells located in the cochlea, and arises simply because the vibrations of the fluid in which they are immersed become too large. The hearing loss resulting from this type of damage should not be confused with nerve deafness, or being "stone-deaf", which is more usually the result of complete failure of the auditory nerve through disease. Rather, we are concerned here with a progressive loss of hearing occurring over periods of perhaps five to ten years.

A measure of the efficiency of hearing is the auditory threshold—that is, the sound pressure level at which we can just begin to detect a sound. As we mentioned in the discussion on units, we chose as a reference sound pressure for the decibel, the threshold for normal hearing, which was 2×10^{-5} N/m². Then if we have normal hearing, our threshold should be just about 0 dB, and this is generally found to be the case for pure tone type sounds at 1000 Hz. As we shall learn later however, when we discuss loudness, the ear is frequency sensitive, and our threshold, even with normal hearing, would be rather more than 0 dB at other frequencies (see fig. 2.6).

Threshold is measured by a process known as "audiometry", in which a pure tone is played via earphones to the subject, and he adjusts the sound pressure level of the tone until it is just perceptible. This level is then his threshold at that frequency. The frequency of the tone is changed and the process repeated. Normally we do not plot the absolute levels that are just perceptible but rather the difference between the threshold and a generally accepted norm which is designated 0 dB. This difference is known as the "threshold shift". A person with good hearing would produce an audiogram, as it is termed, like the one shown in fig. 2.2—that is, his threshold shift is within 5 dB of the norm.

Now, if the subject is exposed to noise of fairly high intensity, say well over 80 dB, for a short period, and is then retested, we will find that his threshold shift has increased markedly at 4 kHz as indicated in fig. 2.2. That is, he has suffered a hearing loss of about, in this example, 20 dB. Note by the way that although nothing was said about the type of noise or its frequency characteristics, the maximum loss is shown to occur at 4 kHz. This is one peculiarity of noise-induced hearing loss. The maximum loss always occurs in the region of 4 kHz.

If we made another test after a few hours, the subject's audiogram would have returned more or less to what it was before exposure to the noise. For that reason we call this loss a temporary threshold shift. If he had been exposed all day to the noise, this temporary threshold shift would have been greater and the period required for recovery would have been longer. Had he been exposed to the noise again before his recovery was complete, the shift from the second exposure would have been slightly more than that from the first. So there is over a period of time a slow build up of, as it were, residual threshold shift. If this repeated exposure has gone on for a long enough period, perhaps two or three years depending on the level of noise, the damage becomes irreversible, and no amount of recovery period will restore normal hearing. We then say that the subject has a permanent threshold shift.

Figure 2.3 shows an example of a large permanent threshold shift which has accumulated over a number of years. What are the practical effects? Oddly enough, people who have this sort of loss often will not admit to being deaf at all, and in a sense this is true in that they can hear some sounds. What has happened though is that as the threshold shift has spread progressively into the speech frequency bands (500 Hz to 4000 Hz) intelligibility starts to be lost, first with the higher frequency speech components like the sharp consonants ("t", "s" etc.), and then other components start to lose their acuity. Eventually speech becomes a meaningless mumble. Whether or not this constitutes "deafness" seems a matter of opinion, but undoubtedly the hearing has ceased to perform its normal function.

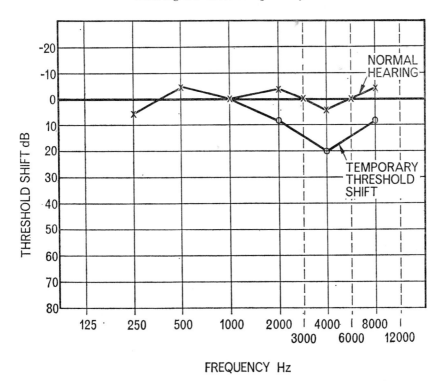

FREQUENCY Hz

Fig. 2.2. Example of temporary hearing loss

One of the more unfortunate characteristics of noise-induced hearing loss is that it is additive to the normal hearing loss which occurs with age—or presbycusis to use the medical term. There is still some doubt as to exactly how much loss occurs naturally over the years, but the curves shown in figure 2.4 give an indication of the order to be expected. This will happen anyway, whether or not the subject has been exposed to noise. The invidious thing about damage-inducing noise is that the type of hearing loss shown in figure 2.3 adds directly to the loss shown in figure 2.4. In effect noise accelerates the onset of natural hearing loss.

We now need to examine the levels of noise to be avoided if cumulative damage of this sort is not to occur. First the factors which are important. Frequency is obviously one. Although damage is nearly always concentrated at 4 kHz, lower frequency noises cause less damage than do higher frequency noises of the same level. Type of noise is another. For the same overall level more damage will be caused if the energy is concentrated at one frequency, than if it is spread over a band of frequencies. The third one is time of exposure. Generally the higher the level, the shorter must be the time of exposure allowed. These factors are summarised in the "Damage Risk Criteria" (DRC) curves shown in fig. 2.5.

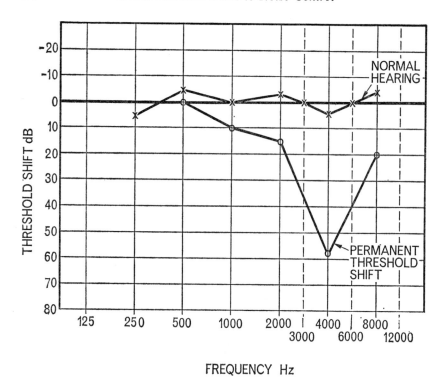

FREQUENCY Hz

Fig. 2.3. Example of permanent hearing loss

Frequency response of the ear and loudness

The lowest frequency which can be identified as sound by a person with normal hearing is about 20 Hz. Lower frequencies can be detected, but it is difficult then to distinguish between hearing, and feeling the "sound" bodily. The highest frequency that the ear can detect is very susceptible to factors like age, health, and as we have seen, history of previous exposure to noise. With acute hearing it could be as high as 20 kHz, but normally the limit seems to be around 16 kHz to 18 kHz.

Although the ear can detect sounds at all frequencies within this range, by no means does it ascribe the same importance to each. In other words, it is very frequency sensitive. This has been demonstrated by a series of tests in which an observer listened to a pure tone sound, having a frequency of 1000 Hz, and some fixed reference level. He then listened to a pure tone of some other frequency, and was asked to adjust the level of the second tone until he judged it to be equal in loudness to the 1000 Hz reference tone. If we plot the envelope of the amplitudes of each of the tones that were judged to be equally as loud as the reference tone, we will obtain a curve like one of the family shown in fig. 2.6, which are called "equal loudness curves". To obtain any other curve it would be necessary only to alter the amplitude of the reference tone.

Taking any one curve then, a sound at any frequency equal in level to the level of the curve at that frequency, will be judged to be equally as loud as sound at any other frequency of level equal to the curve. Marked on each curve is a number of units called "phons". The phon is a unit of loudness, and the rating of any curve in phons is defined as the value of the sound pressure level of that curve at 1000 Hz.

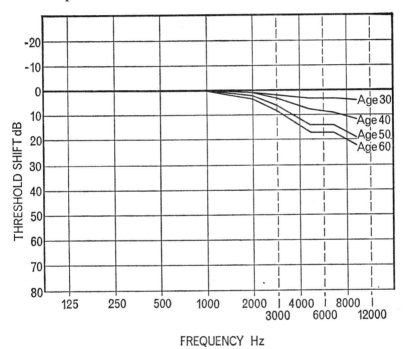

Fig. 2.4. Approximate values of hearing loss due to presbycusis

The dotted curve has special significance as it represents the normal threshold of hearing. The value of sound pressure level at about 2000 Hz is zero, which means, if we look back to the discussion on units, that the sound pressure is $2 \times 10^{-5} \, \text{N/m}^2$. The negative values of sound pressure level on this curve have no real significance. They merely show that between 2 kHz and about 5 kHz, the ear is capable of detecting sound pressures which are less than $2 \times 10^{-5} \, \text{N/m}^2$.

The equal loudness curves tell us some interesting things about human hearing. First, for sounds of generally low amplitude there is a very

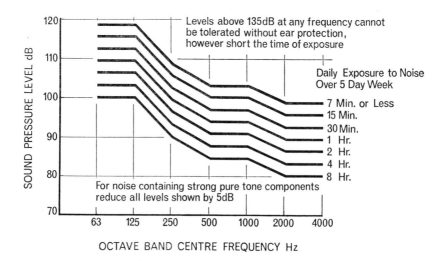

OCTAVE BAND CENTRE FREQUENCY Hz

Fig. 2.5. Sound pressure levels at which hearing conservation measures should be introduced

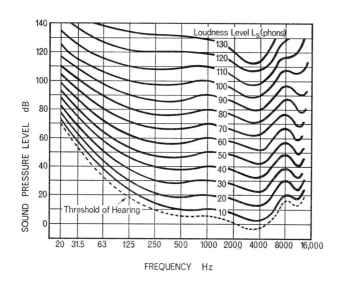

FREQUENCY   Hz

Fig. 2.6. Equal loudness contours

marked frequency sensitivity—a sound at 30 Hz would have to be about 50 dB higher than a sound at 1000 Hz to be judged equally as loud. On the other hand this apparently huge insensitivity to low frequency sound is dependent upon the amplitude. When the sound pressure level is over about 80 dB at 1000 Hz, the level at 30 Hz which would be judged equally as loud, would be only about 15 dB higher. This non-linearity of subjective judgement with amplitude means that one does not make a sound "twice as loud" by doubling the intensity (i.e. by increasing the sound pressure level by 3 dB). If we were to carry out a subjective test on how loudness changes with changes of sound pressure, we would find that to make a sound appear twice as loud we would have to increase the sound pressure level by about 10 dB.

Subjective units

We see then, that the ear responds not only to the absolute sound pressure level of a sound, but also to its frequency content. It gives a weighting to the level of sound according to this frequency content, and ascribes to it a certain loudness. This means of course, that if we want to know how a person will judge the sound, we somehow have to translate our objective measured units of sound pressure level and frequency content into subjective units of loudness.

If we were dealing only with pure tones it would be simple. We would plot their amplitudes on the family of curves in fig. 2.6, and the highest curve they touched would be their loudness in phons. Unfortunately most of the everyday noises we deal with are more complex. If pure tones are present at all they are usually mixed up with a more "random" type of noise having a broad frequency spectrum.

We could carry out a similar series of tests as those summarised by fig. 2.6, using bands of random noise as the test and reference signals, but the additional variables of bandwidth, and spectrum shape within the band, make it a very difficult and involved procedure. The other possibility is to calculate the phon level of a complex sound. A number of methods for calculating the loudness of a sound from its measured frequency spectrum have been proposed, all of which, in essence, consist of weighting the sound pressure level of each band according to its frequency range. The individual band is then accorded a loudness level, and the total loudness level is simply a sum of the loudness level of each of the bands.

Unfortunately, while these methods do produce results which line up well with observed subjective reaction, the procedure is time-consuming and sometimes tedious. What we really need is a loudness meter from which the loudness level can be read directly.

What happens with an objective sound meter? It accepts all the frequency components of the sound, and adds all their absolute levels together to give an overall sound intensity (sound pressure level). Our loudness meter however must do more than this. It would still need all the components of the sound that were present. (Most microphones do this anyway). It would then need to reflect somehow the frequency sensitivity of the ear. That is, it would have to attenuate the lower frequency components before adding them to the higher frequency components. The resulting overall sound pressure level would then be a "weighted" level.

The point is, which frequencies have to be attenuated and by how much? In fact, it is found that the shapes of the equal loudness curves shown in fig. 2.6, give a fairly good representation of the amount of weighting needed for the various frequency components of even complex sounds—in spite of the fact that they were obtained using pure tones. It now becomes a relatively simple matter to build into our amplifier a frequency sensitive attenuating network which is the inverse of an equal loudness curve. In fact, we need more than one weighting network to cover the whole range of sound amplitude because as we can see from fig. 2.6, the curves get flatter as sound pressure level increases.

Three weighting curves have now been internationally agreed, and they are referred to as "A", for sound pressure levels up to 55 dB, "B" for sound pressure levels between 55 and 85 dB and "C" for levels above 85 dB. The actual levels measured by these networks are denoted respectively, dBA, dBB, and dBC, and any figure quoted must be qualified as to which network was used. The shapes of the curves are shown in fig. 2.7.

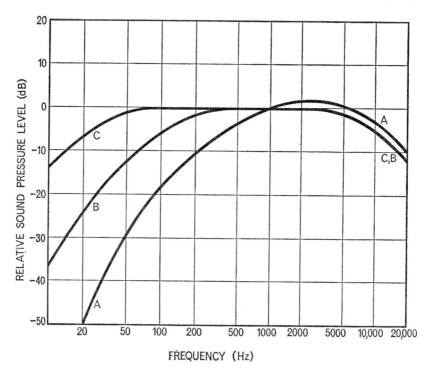

Fig. 2.7. International standard A, B, and C weighting curves for sound level meters

Now we have a further problem. If we measure the noise in terms of a single figure, however representative its weighting shape may be, it tells us virtually nothing about the frequency content. Why do we want to know? The frequency content of the noise may not give us any more assistance in assessing its acceptability than does the weighted overall level—providing it *is* acceptable. But as soon as the noise is found to be excessive, we need to know more than the single figure can give us.

We need to know for example why it is excessive. Is the noise too high over the whole frequency spectrum, or are there just one or two frequency components which are excessive? This information is vital to the noise control engineer because, as we shall see later, most noise control techniques are frequency dependent. So, even if we make an initial assessment using a single figure like the dBA, we will almost certainly have to follow it up with some sort of frequency analysis. In fact this often happens. Sound level meters equipped to measure only dBA, dBB, dBC and linear unweighted levels are relatively inexpensive and very useful for making preliminary assessments, during commissioning for example. When excessive noise is found, the more sophisticated instrumentation capable of frequency analysis can be called in to pinpoint the trouble.

It would be more convenient though, if we could make the same sort of assessment as say the dBA does, and at the same time obtain some information on the frequency content. We can do this by using a family of "Noise Criteria" (NC) curves which were originally developed in the United States to predict acceptable noise levels for offices. Basically they consist of a family of octave band spectra, each with its own rating number (fig. 2.8). The octave band spectrum of the noise in question is plotted on the same grid, and the "NC" rating of the noise is the highest NC curve touched.

The similarity of the shape of the NC curves with that of the equal loudness curves is evident, and in fact the NC rating of a noise gives us a very good guide to its loudness. It also tells us something about its capacity to interfere with speech communication. The NC curves were based on a survey in office-type spaces where speech communication was important. A measure of suitability of an environment for speech is the "speech interference level" (SIL) defined as the average of the sound pressure levels in the three octave bands between 500 Hz and 2000 Hz—the most critical bands for speech. Table 2.2 shows typical values of speech interference levels for a male voice. Female voice levels are about 5 dB less than the value shown.

The result of the survey showed that SIL alone was not a good guide to whether the occupants considered the rooms to be acceptable. Even if the SIL was low enough for reasonable conversation, people would still complain if the loudness level was too high. This led to the finding that loudness level and SIL had to be within a certain amount of each other.

Accordingly the curves of fig. 2.8 were constructed to preserve this relationship. The number following the NC on any curve is the speech

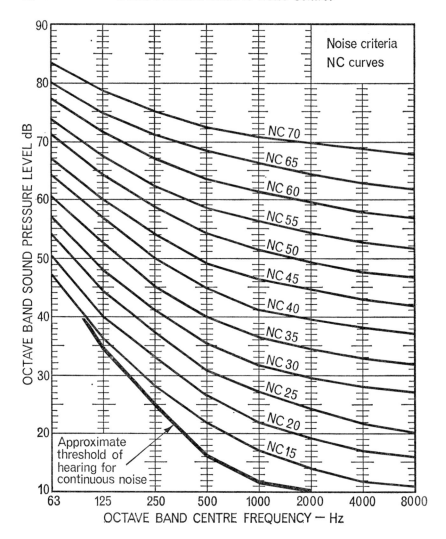

Fig. 2.8. Noise criteria curves

interference level in dB, and the loudness in phons is always (SIL + 22).

The actual value of SIL or indeed loudness is not however important in itself—nowadays they are very rarely referred to. What *is* important is the fact that, if we have assigned to a certain environment a maximum permissible NC rating, and we then find our measured octave band spectrum exceeds it, we know at once which frequency components require control.

Because of the source of the information which led to NC curves, they are particularly suitable for assessing office environments and are widely used in ventilating and air conditioning work.

TABLE 2.2
Speech interference levels (SIL) in dB

Distance between speaker and listener	Voice level			
Metres	*Normal*	*Raised*	*Very loud*	*Shouting*
0·15	71	77	83	89
0·3	65	71	77	83
0·6	59	65	71	77
0·9	55	61	67	73
1·2	53	59	65	71
1·5	51	57	63	69
1·8	49	55	61	67
3·7	43	49	55	61

More recently, a similar series of curves were developed in Europe, and intended for more general use, especially for predicting community reaction to noise. These are called "Noise rating" (NR) curves, and are shown in fig. 2.9. They are currently being adopted by the International Standard Organisation, and tend to be the more widely used in Europe. For engineering purposes there is very little to choose between NC and NR curves.

The dBA, NC curves and NR curves, are all subjective units which give us a fair representation of how the ear actually assesses noise. Now we have to fix limiting values to them for different environments.

Criteria for various environments

Whenever we speak of noise criteria, there is one important point that must always be borne in mind. Sound pressure levels that have been recommended for particular situations are intended as a guide to average acceptability only. A tolerance of about 5 dB should always be allowed for. For example, if we say that for a certain type of room the criterion should be NC40, we may very well find that many people judge it to be acceptable if the actual level is NC45. And, almost certainly we would find someone who would say it was unacceptable even if the actual level were NC35.

Where the risk is hearing damage, such as in heavy industrial environments, the curves shown in figure 2.5 may be taken as criteria for deciding whether the noise is excessive. Here, no tolerance should be allowed. If the levels are equal or even very close to the values shown, taking into account the length of time an operator is exposed, action should be taken to reduce the risk—either by reducing the noise, or by seeking expert assistance for a more detailed investigation.

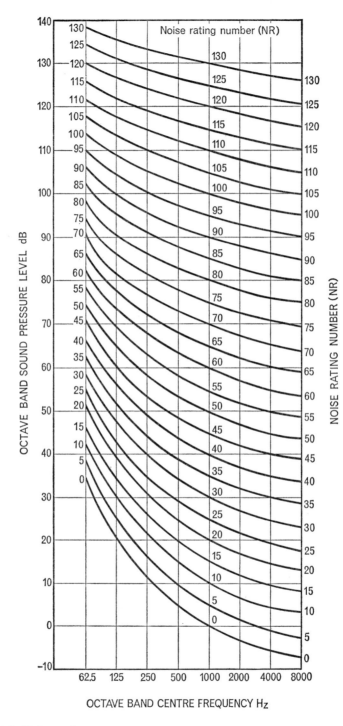

OCTAVE BAND CENTRE FREQUENCY Hz

Fig. 2.9. Noise rating curves

For office-type environments, as we have seen, the NC curves have been specifically designed to combine the requirements of speech interference and loudness levels. The recommended criteria for a wide range of usage is shown in Table 2.3. As an alternative, the NR curves may be used as recommended in Table 2.4.

TABLE 2.3

Recommended NC levels for various environments

Environment	Range of NC levels likely to be acceptable
Factories (heavy engineering)	55–75
Factories (light engineering)	45–65
Kitchens	40–50
Swimming baths and sports areas	35–50
Department stores and shops	35–45
Restaurants, bars, cafeterias and canteens	35–45
Mechanised offices	40–50
General offices	35–45
Private offices, libraries, courtrooms and schoolrooms	30–35
Homes, bedrooms	25–35
Hospital wards and operating theatres	25–35
Cinemas	30–35
Theatres, assembly halls and churches	25–30
Concert and opera halls	20–25
Broadcasting and recording studios	15–20

TABLE 2.4

Recommended NR levels for various environments

Workshops	NR 60–70
Mechanised offices	NR 50–55
Gymnasia, sports halls, swimming baths	NR 40–50
Restaurants, bars, cafeterias	NR 35–45
Private offices, libraries, courtrooms	NR 30–40
Cinemas, hospitals, churches, small conference rooms	NR 25–35
Class rooms, T.V. studios, large conference rooms	NR 20–30
Concert halls, theatres	NR 20–25
Diagnostic clinics, audiometric rooms	NR 10–20

In residential areas the problem is rather more complex. People who may be prepared to spend their working hours in, say, a fairly busy office or a workshop without any thought of noise, would be very annoyed if anything like those noise levels were maintained at home—especially during the night. However low the SIL or even loudness level may be, if the noise is intrusive upon their privacy it is likely to cause annoyance.

D

In fact both dBA and NR curves give good indications of the type of noise people will tolerate in their homes, but because of the highly subjective nature of the problem, both need some qualification before we can say that a certain dBA level or Noise Rating will be acceptable.

We have to take into account various environmental factors and indeed, the aural character of the noise itself. For example, a noise containing a pure tone superimposed upon a random type broad frequency band noise, will be more annoying than the broad band noise by itself, even if the energy in the pure tone is too small to contribute to a weighted overall level. The same can be said for any other aurally recognisable characteristics like a "hiss" or a "screech". Intermittency or impulsiveness in the noise makes it more annoying than the same level of continuous noise. Again, a given noise would be more annoying if it occurred in a quiet suburb, than if it occurred in the middle of a large city. Day or night-time noises, summer or winter (windows open or closed), all have to be taken into account.

The first and perhaps most authoritative step in this country towards firm—based recommendations for the acceptability of noise to householders was the report of the Wilson Committee on the problem of noise. This report gave recommendations in terms of dBA, not only for acceptable background noise, but also for assessing the effects of additional noises coming, for example, from nearby industrial premises.

Much of what was recommended by the Wilson Committee has been incorporated in the more recent British Standard 4142:1967, "Method of Rating Industrial Noise Affecting Mixed Residential and Industrial Areas". The essence of this system is that the existing background (measured in dBA) is preferred as the criterion. If the planned new noise, after being suitably weighted as shown in Table 2.5, is more than 10 dBA above the background, complaints may be expected. If it is less than 5 dBA above, the situation is described as "marginal". If the problem already exists, and the background cannot be measured with the offending noise absent, the Standard recommends a basic criterion of 50 dBA be used, and then weighted to take into account various environmental factors, as shown in Table 2.5.

If we need more detail for an assessment of community reaction to noise, we can use the octave band method of NR curves. Again the method is essentially to compare a noise with a background level, but in this case all the weighting factors are applied to the basic criterion, rather than some to the noise and some to the background.

The relevant corrections are in Table 2.6. Again, less than 5 between the criterion NR and the measured octave band NR is marginal, 5 to 10 is "difficult to accept", and greater than 10 can be assumed to be unacceptable. Note: with the "NR" method the criterion is expressed as an NR curve to be met *inside* the residence. To determine the corresponding criterion outside, it is usually sufficiently accurate to add to the NR number, 10 for times when the windows are closed, and 5 when they are open.

TABLE 2.5

Summary of recommendations of BS 4142:1967

Noise level

Subject noise to be measured in dBA outside the residential building affected.

Correction for noise character

Tonal character—if the noise has definite continuous note (whine, hiss, squeal etc.)
   add 5 dBA to measured level.

Impulsive character—if the noise contains irregularities like bangs, clanks, thumps, etc.
   or if it is irregular enough to attract attention, add 5 dBA to measured level.

Intermittency—If the noise is not continuous, subtract the following dBA levels from
   the measured level.

(Note: these corrections have been rounded to nearest 5 dBA as a guide. For detailed
corrections consult BS 4142-1967).

| *On-time* | *No. of times occurring in* 8 *hour period* | | | | | |
| *duration* | | *Day or evening* | | | *Night* (10 *p.m.*–7 *a.m.*) | |
secs.	1	10	100	1	10	100
1	35	30	25	25	20	15
2	30	30	20	20	15	10
5	30	25	15	15	10	10
10	25	20	10	15	10	5
20	20	15	10	10	5	5
60	15	10	5	5	5	0
120	10	10	5	5	0	0
300	10	5	0	0	0	0

Corrected noise level is measured noise level plus the appropriate corrections.

Background

If ambient background level outside residential building affected cannot be measured
in the absence of the noise, the following procedure should be followed:

Take as basic criterion	50 dBA

Corrections to be added to basic level

(a) Type of installation causing noise

(i) New factory	0 dBA
(ii) Existing factory in which noise radiated outside is changed by alteration to the building, or the installation of new plant	0 dBA
(iii) Existing factory not typical of the area, or obviously not in any of the other categories	+ 5 dBA
(iv) Old established factories completely in character in well established industrial areas	+10 dBA

(b) Type of area (select one only)

Rural (residential)	− 5 dBA
Suburban, little road traffic	0 dBA
Urban residential	+ 5 dBA
Predominantly residential urban, but with some light industry or road traffic	+10 dBA
General industrial area	+15 dBA
Predominantly industrial area (few dwellings)	+20 dBA

(c) Time of day

Weekdays only 8 a.m. to 6 p.m.	+ 5 dBA
Night 10 p.m. to 7 a.m.	− 5 dBA
All other times	0 dBA

(d) Season

If it is known that noise occurs only during the winter	+ 5 dBA

Corrected criterion is basic criterion plus the appropriate corrections.

Assessment

If the corrected measured noise level exceeds the corrected criterion by 10 dBA, complaints may be expected.

If the corrected measured noise level is more than 10 dBA below the corrected criterion, complaints are not likely to arise.

Differences of 5 dBA or less are of marginal significance.

TABLE 2.6

Summary of the method of assessing community reaction based on NR curves.
(After Kosten and Van Os)

Selection of criterion	
Basic criterion for inside sleeping rooms	NR 25
Basic criterion for inside living rooms	NR 30
Corrections to be added to the basic NR number	
Pure tone or other tonal characteristic easily distinguishable	− 5
Impulsive and/or intermittent noise	− 5
Noise only during working hours	+ 5
Noise occurring only 25 % of time	+ 5
6 %	+10
1·5 %	+15
0·5 %	+20
0·1 %	+25
0·02 %	+30
Type of area, very quiet suburban	− 5
Suburban	0
Residential urban	+ 5
Urban near some industry	+10
Area of heavy industry	+15
Corrected criterion is basic criterion plus appropriate corrections.	

Assessment

If the measured octave band spectrum exceeds the corrected NR criterion curve in any octave band by less than 5 dB, the noise is rated marginal

by 5 to 10 dB the noise is rated difficult to accept

by greater than 10 dB the noise is rated unacceptable.

CHAPTER 3

The measurement of acoustic properties

In the course of assessing any noise problem, sooner or later we will find ourselves involved in some sort of calculation. We may for example want to predict the level of noise from new factory plant. We may want to estimate how noise from a plant room will travel through a building. Or we may need to select a silencer for a ventilating system.

Whatever the problem, we will find, as the next chapters show, that some quantities appear repeatedly in almost all the important calculations. Those we shall be most concerned with are,

Sound Power Level

Directivity Index

Sound Reduction Index

Insertion Loss

Absorption Coefficient

If we know these quantities, most of our noise problems are calculable, at least to a sufficient degree of accuracy for engineering purposes. It will be of help in providing the background to the procedures for assessing a noise problem, if we first learn of the more usual ways in which these key quantities are measured.

The measurement of sound power level

We shall find when we look into methods of assessing noise that almost all of our calculations hinge on the sound power level of the offending source. The reason that so much emphasis is placed on sound power is that this is the one datum quantity of a piece of machinery or plant, that does not change with environment.*

If we were to measure the sound pressure level from a machine in one environment, and then moved it to a quite different one—say from the middle of a large open space to inside a small factory building—we would find that the sound pressure level at the same distance from the machine had changed, perhaps considerably. The sound power level of the machine on the other hand would not have changed, and it is this fact which enables us to predict before the move takes place, what the new sound pressure level will be.

Sound power can be measured in a number of ways. Usually, the method falls into one of the following categories.

---

* In some special cases, the new environment may have the effect of physically changing the noise generating mechanisms, and hence the amount of sound power radiated. In industrial acoustics however, such cases are rare, or at least the amount by which sound power output is affected, is not significant.

Free field testing

As its name suggests, the environment of this type of test is completely free of reflecting surfaces. It becomes necessary when the source noise has strong pure tone characteristics, or when additional information is required on the spatial pattern of the radiated sound. The principle of the free field method of measuring sound power is exactly as outlined in Chapter 1. That is, we enclose the source in an imaginary control surface, evaluate local intensity (energy flow rate per unit area) at a number of points on the surface from direct measurement of sound pressure, and sum them to give the total power produced. To do this however we must make our measurements at a point where there is a definite simple relationship between energy and measured sound pressure, like that shown in equation (1.3). If we measure too close to the source we will find, particularly if the dimensions of the source are many times the wavelength of the sound being generated, that there is no simple relationship. This means we must make the radius of our control sphere large enough to ensure that by the time they reach the surface of the sphere the sound waves are radiating freely and progressively outward from the source.

We also have to ensure that what we are measuring is only the sound travelling radially *outward*. If we have any reflecting surfaces in the vicinity, we may also be measuring a contribution from sound waves travelling in a different direction after having undergone one or more reflections. Obviously this would not give us a true assessment of the sound energy actually radiated from the source. Ideally, we would suspend the source high in the air, its distance from the ground being many times the longest wavelength (lowest frequency) we are concerned with. Not very practicable, but we can still perform a free field test with the source at ground level providing there are no nearby obstructions like large buildings. Even this is not very convenient, the success of the tests being completely at the mercy of the weather.

It is more usual to carry out free field testing by suspending the source in the centre of a specially constructed room known as an "anechoic chamber". This is a room of size dependent upon the dimensions of the largest source which will require testing, specially constructed to give high insulation against extraneous noise from any other sources which may be outside the room, e.g. aircraft or traffic. The inside surfaces of the room are lined with an acoustically absorptive treatment to eliminate reflections. In other words the objective is to have the sound energy radiated from the source as near completely absorbed as possible when it first strikes a wall or a ceiling, so that virtually none is reflected back into the room. In this way it is possible to simulate outdoor conditions. Figure 3.1 shows a typical construction suitable for free field testing industrial fans.

We have already outlined (see Chapter 1) the principle of calculating sound power from sound pressure levels measured in a free field. We considered a source radiating uniformly in all directions, of such power

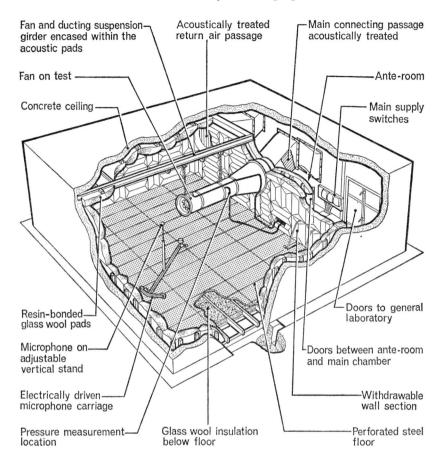

Fan and ducting suspension—
girder encased within the
acoustic pads

Acoustically treated
return air passage

Main connecting passage
acoustically treated

Fan on test

Ante-room

Concrete ceiling

Main supply
switches

Resin-bonded
glass wool pads

Doors to general
laboratory

Microphone on
adjustable
vertical stand

Doors between ante-room
and main chamber

Electrically driven
microphone carriage

Withdrawable
wall section

Pressure measurement
location

Glass wool insulation
below floor

Perforated steel
floor

Fig. 3.1. Construction details of an industrial free-field room

that the sound pressure was p at any point on the surface of an imaginary sphere of radius r. Then we found that the total power produced by the source was given by

$$W = p^2/\varrho c \,.\, 4\pi r^2 \tag{3.1}$$

The result came out in this form because the intensity was everywhere the same on the control surface. If it had not been the same (as is more usually the case), we would have measured the sound pressure p at a large number of points on the sphere, and evaluated the integral in equation (1.5).

This does tend to be a tedious procedure however, and except for research type work, or where the source has a very directional radiation pattern, it is not really necessary. Instead we divide the surface of our control sphere into a number of elemental areas δA_1, δA_2, δA_3 ... etc. We then measure the sound pressure in the centre of each of the elemental areas, and assume that this pressure is uniform over the element. From this we have the corresponding sound intensity over the element from equation (1.3). If we call the intensity over each element I_1, I_2, I_3 ... etc., then the total power generated by the source is

$$W = I_1.\delta A_1 + I_2 . \delta A_2 + I_3 . \delta A_3 \ldots \text{etc.} \qquad (3.2)$$

The only difficulty here is to decide upon how many elemental areas to choose. This depends upon how directional the radiation pattern is—a highly directional source will obviously require more "sampling" points than one which is very nearly unidirectional. In any case, to simplify the calculations we usually make our elemental areas equal. Then the total power becomes

$$W = \delta A \left[I_1 + I_2 + I_3 + \ldots \text{etc.} \right] \qquad (3.3)$$

Some examples of convenient arrays of measuring points are shown in fig. 3.2.

Co·ordinates of mid-points of sectors			
Sector numbers	Co·ordinate		
	X	Y	Z
1-8	±1/√3	±1/√3	±1/√3
9-12	±0.934	±0.357	0
13-16	0	±0.934	±0.357
17-20	±0.357	0	±0.934

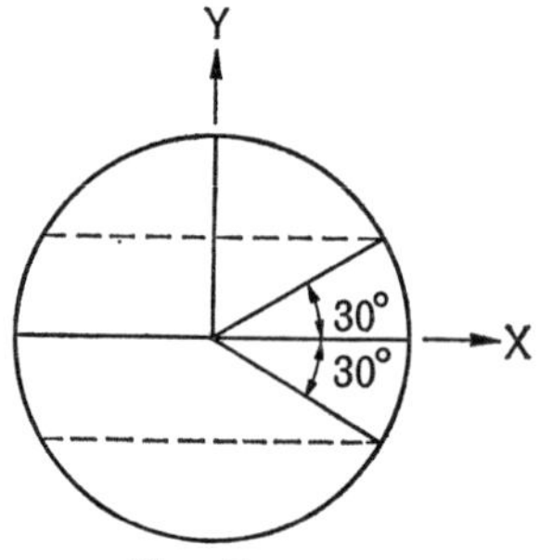

Elevation

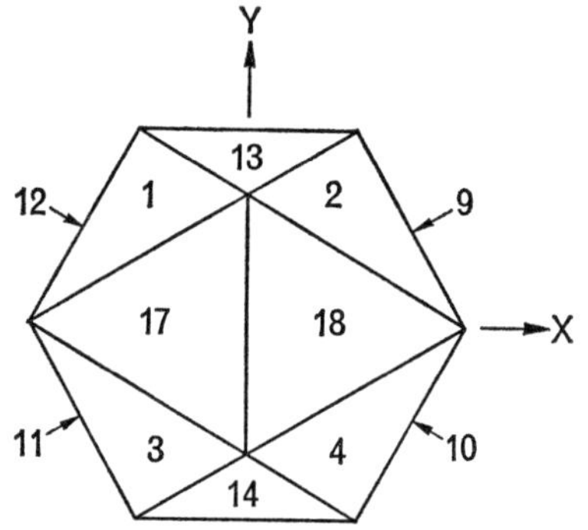

View from top of sphere

(a)

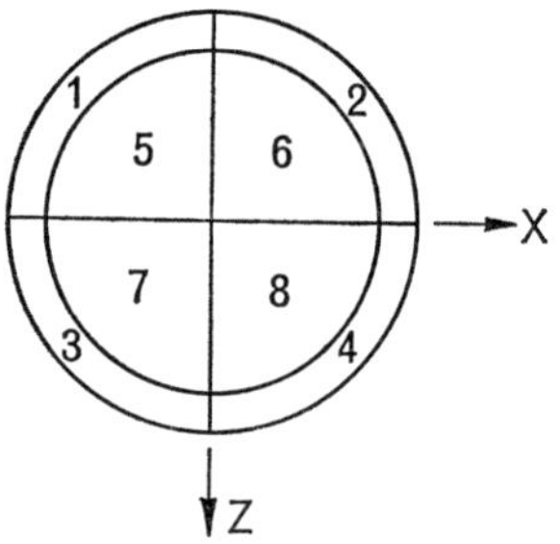

Plan view

(b)

Fig. 3.2. (a) Division of a spherical surface into 20 equal areas of identical shape

(b) Division of a sphere into 16 parts of equal area but unequal shape

Life becomes very much more simple if we are dealing with a source whose radiation pattern is axisymmetric—a fan for example. Then our elemental areas become "bands" around the sphere—like zones of latitude —and we have to make only one measurement in each zone, usually in the horizontal plane. Figure 3.3 shows how the zones can be arranged.

How the sound power levels are presented depends upon the use to which the information is put. The most common presentation is in terms of the octave band sound power levels. That is the total sound power level in each of the standard octave bands of frequency listed in Table 1.5. To obtain this, an octave band analysis of sound pressure level must be made at each measuring position, and the sound power level is evaluated separately for each frequency band.

A single figure overall sound power level is sometimes given, but this should not be encouraged, since information on the frequency content of the noise will almost certainly be required later, if any assessment is to be made of the effects of the noise.

Occasionally one requires more detail on frequency content than even the octave band spectrum provides—in which case a one-third octave band analysis can be used. Single frequency ("narrow-band") analysis is required usually only when the source has strong discrete frequency components ("pure tones").

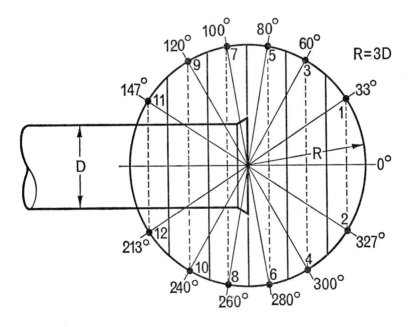

Fig. 3.3. Microphone positions for zones of equal area when axial symmetry exists

Reverberant field testing

With a free field test we get a little more information about the source than its overall sound power level. In the course of measuring the distribution of sound pressure level around it, we also find out its directivity pattern—whether, in fact, it is radiating a large proportion of its energy in any particular direction. This information however is not always needed. Add that to the fact that anechoic rooms are usually very expensive to construct, and the advantages of some alternative method of test can be seen.

The philosophy behind the free field method of measuring sound power was to take some sort of control surface through which the energy must pass and, as it were, to count the rate of energy flow. As long as we have enclosed the source, and made sure that none of its energy can get by undetected, we will have measured all its power. We can get the same answer in a different manner. A feature of the anechoic chamber was that its walls were highly absorptive so that once a sound wave had left the source, if we had not measured its intensity before it reached a wall, we could not have measured it at all—simply because all (or most) of it would have been absorbed by the wall lining. If now we remove all the lining so that the wall is highly reflective, then each time a sound wave strikes a surface of the room, while some of its energy will still be absorbed in the wall, most of it will be reflected. The reflected wave carries on until it strikes a second surface and the process is repeated. This is happening of course to all the sound waves radiated by the source, so there is a continuous extraction of acoustic energy from the room. But this energy extraction can only continue until its rate is balanced by the rate of energy input to the room, i.e. the sound power of the source.

By this time many reflections will have occurred, and statistically the

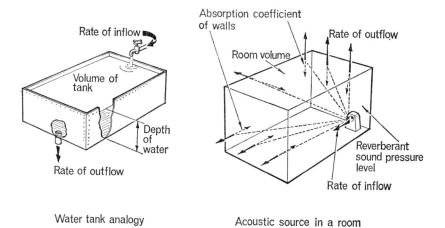

Water tank analogy   Acoustic source in a room

Fig. 3.4. Reverberant sound pressure level

energy density—energy per unit volume—throughout the room (except close to the source) will be roughly constant. Under these conditions the sound field in the room is said to be diffuse. Provided our "reverberant" room, as it is called, is designed to give us a truly diffuse field, we can relate the energy density of this field directly to the sound power produced by the source.

A good analogy here would be a water tank, supplied by a tap, and having an open drain (Fig. 3.4). Here the tank represents the room, and the tap supplying it, the source. The drain represents the rate of removal of energy from the incident sound wave due to the absorption of the walls.

Clearly we can relate the level of water in the tank (sound pressure), to the volume of water flowing in (source sound power), if we take into account the volume of the tank (room volume) and the rate of flow in the drain (absorption of the room surfaces).

The volume of the room is straightforward enough, but what about the absorption? We shall be discussing how to calculate absorption later, but for this type of problem it is more convenient to work in terms of "reverberation time", which is directly related to absorption. If we suddenly switch off our source, the level in the room does not decay instantaneously. Obviously the last few waves to leave the source will have to undergo a few reflections before they die out completely, and this takes time. How long it takes depends on how absorptive the walls are—the more reflective they are the longer is the time for the sound to decay. This decay time is called the reverberation time, and is defined as the time taken for the sound pressure level to decay 60 dB. So, as a measure of energy extraction rate from the room, reverberation time and absorption are interchangeable.

The procedure for obtaining sound power level in a reverberant room is very simple. The source is placed in the room, where volume and reverberation time will be known, and the sound pressure level is measured at a number of points in the room to ensure that a fair sample of the intensity of the diffuse field has been obtained. Then the sound power level of the source is simply

$$SWL = SPL + 10 \log V - 10 \log T - 14 \text{ dB} \qquad (3.4)$$

where SPL is the average sound pressure level in the room

V is the room volume m³

T is the reverberation time secs.

Again, if a frequency spectra of sound power level is required, sound pressure level must be analysed into the required frequency bands at each measuring point, and the average sound pressure level obtained at each frequency separately. It may well be found that the number of measuring points required to get a fair average is more for some frequencies than for others. Also, since reverberation time is usually a function of frequency, the value for the particular frequency being considered must be used.

Semi-reverberant field testing

While we can measure sound power very accurately with an anechoic chamber, or with a reverberant room, they both require a special construction which makes them rather expensive. Too expensive perhaps to be regarded as a general industrial facility. Fortunately, it is still possible to obtain a value of SWL sufficiently accurate for most engineering purposes with a semi-reverberant room. As its name implies, it lies in terms of acoustic properties somewhere between the fully absorptive anechoic room and the fully reflective reverberant room. In fact, most rooms are semi-reverberant. The fact that we can obtain sound power from a semi-reverberant room, makes the method an attractive one for machine manufacturers. The tests could easily be carried out in a development laboratory for example.

Most semi-reverberant test procedures call for a substitution test. In this we have to use a standard noise generator, which has been previously calibrated so that its sound power level is known. This standard source is placed in the room and the sound level is sampled at a number of points to ensure a fair average is obtained. The standard source is then replaced by the test source, and the measurements are repeated. The test source power level will then differ from the standard source power level (which of course is known), by the same amount in decibels as the difference between the average sound pressure level in the room with the test source running, and that with the standard source running. If the standard source power in a particular frequency band is SWL_s, and it produces a sound pressure level in that band SPL_s in the room, and if the test machine produces a level in the same band of SPL_T, then the sound power level of the machine SWL_T in the band is given by:

$$SWL_T = SWL_s + (SPL_T - SPL_s) \text{ dB} \qquad (3.5)$$

A summary of these test methods is given in British Standard 4196:1967.

Duct testing

We have now considered two methods of measuring the energy of a source. In the free field method we enclosed it in an imaginary surface, and examined the distribution of intensity over the surface to make sure we had a representative sample of all the energy passing through. In the reverberant room method we constrained all the energy to appear in an enclosed volume (the room) so we could sample its density and hence estimate how much there was in the whole room. The semi-reverberant method was much the same, except that we had to calibrate it first by using a source of known output.

A third alternative is to constrain all the energy to pass along a rigid

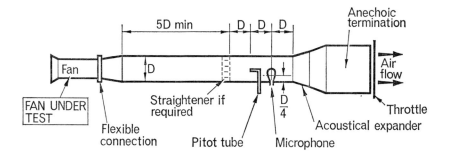

Fig. 3.5. The in-duct method for determining sound power level of a fan

walled pipe or duct. Here we are combining the "constraining" idea of the reverberant room (the duct), with the control surface of the free field (a sectional plane of the duct). Many machines are ideally suited for in-duct testing—large fans for example. The fan is simply connected to a long duct along which all the energy it produces must travel. At some distance along the duct we choose a measuring plane, and the average sound pressure level in the frequency band required is determined by measuring at a number of points on the plane. The total power in that band travelling along the duct (and hence the sound power level of the fan at that frequency) is given by

$$\text{SWL} = \text{SPL} + 10 \log S \quad \text{dB} \tag{3.6}$$

where SPL is the average sound pressure level across the plane of measurements dB

S is the cross-sectional area of the duct at the plane of measurement m².

The result stems directly from equation (1.7), when consistent units are used.

While this is basically the procedure, certain precautions must be observed when performing in-duct tests. First, if it is a fan we are testing, the microphone must be fitted with a windshield. Otherwise, aerodynamic pressure fluctuations on the microphone diaphragm, due to the passage of the air over it, will add to and be indistinguishable from acoustic pressure fluctuations.

Secondly once the energy has passed the measuring plane, we have to ensure that none is reflected back up the duct from the end to give an artificially high reading. Sound energy would be reflected from the end of the tube if it were left as a plain end. This is because the acoustic impedance inside the tube is rather different from the impedance in the large volume of air outside. When an acoustic wave in any medium meets a change of impedance some of the energy is always reflected.

We shall see what factors determine how much energy is reflected when we come on to discuss noise in ventilating systems. For the moment we need only say that when we are assessing sound power by measuring in a duct, all reflected energy must be kept to a minimum. First we have to provide an expansion duct at the end to give a gradual change from the duct impedance to the open air impedance. Normally these are exponential in contour. The other thing we have to avoid is sound getting out from the end of the duct and then being reflected back into it by some nearby hard surface. To do this we provide what is known as an "anechoic termination", which is in effect a sort of miniature anechoic chamber fitted over the end of the expansion duct. Figure 3.5 shows a typical arrangement for determining the sound power of a fan, following the recommendations of British Standard 848 Part 2.

The measurement of Directivity Index

In any measurement of sound power by a free field test the information necessary to evaluate Directivity Index in any angular direction, θ (normally written DI(θ)), will have been measured as a matter of course. It is defined by

$$DI(\theta) = 10 \log Q_\theta \text{ dB} \qquad (3.7)$$

where Q_θ is the "directivity factor", defined as the ratio of the sound intensity in the direction θ, to the sound intensity at the same distance from the source averaged over all angles θ. The average intensity is the intensity that would be produced at that distance by a spherically radiating source of the same power. This is easily calculated from equation (1.6). Hence if the total power is W, the average intensity is $W/4\pi r^2$.

Then if the sound pressure at a point distance r from the source and angle θ to the axis is p(θ), the directivity factor in the direction θ is

$$Q_\theta = \frac{P(\theta)^2}{\varrho c} \cdot \frac{4\pi r^2}{W} \qquad (3.8)$$

In decibel notation, it can be shown that when appropriate reference quantities are inserted in equation (3.8), the Directivity Index is given by

$$DI(\theta) = SPL(\theta) - SPL_{av} \qquad (3.9)$$

where SPL(θ) is the sound pressure level measured in a particular frequency band at the point distance r from the source, and angle θ to the axis, and SPL_{av} is the space average sound pressure level in that frequency band which would be produced at the same distance by a source which radiated the same amount of acoustic power uniformly in all directions (see Chapter 4).

The measurement of Sound Reduction Index

The sound reduction index, R, of a wall or panel is a measure of its ability to prevent acoustic energy passing through it. We shall come on to discuss in later chapters the behaviour of a panel on to which sound waves are impinging. For the moment it will suffice to say that sound reduction index is defined as

$$R = 10 \log (1/\tau) \text{ dB} \qquad (3.10)$$

where τ is the "transmission coefficient", defined as the ratio of the acoustic energy transmitted through the panel, to the total energy incident upon it.

Sound reduction index is a property only of the panel (and the way in which it is mounted). In that sense it is a datum quantity rather like sound power level, which, except in some special cases does not alter with the environment in which the panel is placed. As we shall see in the next chapter, this quantity is of fundamental importance when we are trying to predict the behaviour of sound passing into or out of rooms.

The laboratory measurement of the sound reduction index of a panel requires two adjoining reverberant rooms, separated by a common wall having a very high value of R (fig. 3.6). The test panel or wall section is then fixed into an opening in the party wall. One of the chambers is used as a "source room", by setting up in it a diffuse field, with the aid of a sound source such as an array of loudspeakers, and the other then becomes the "receiving room".

If we call the average sound pressure level in the source room L_1, and that in the receiving room L_2, then the sound reduction index is given by

$$R = L_1 - L_2 + 10 \log S - 10 \log A \quad \text{dB} \qquad (3.11)$$

where S is the area of the test panel m²

A is the absorption in the receiving room m² units

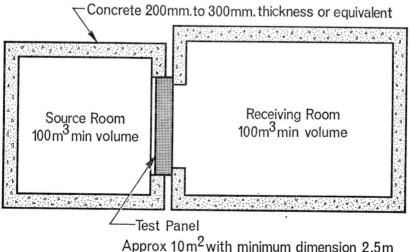

Concrete 200mm. to 300mm. thickness or equivalent

Source Room
100m³ min volume

Receiving Room
100m³ min volume

Test Panel
Approx 10m² with minimum dimension 2.5m

Fig. 3.6. Arrangement of room for measuring sound reduction index (to BS 2750:1956)

The reason for including S and A in the evaluation of sound reduction index, is explained in the discussion on room calculations in Chapter 4, as is the method of estimating A.

The preferred method of describing sound reduction index is a curve of its value plotted at the centre frequencies of the standard one-third octave bands listed in Table 1.5, from 100 Hz to 3150 Hz inclusive. This requires measurements of L_1 and L_2 in one-third octave bands, and values of A at each of the centre frequencies.

Occasionally an "average sound reduction index" will suffice, in which case the value quoted is the arithmetic mean of the decibel values between 100 Hz and 3150 Hz.

The measurement of Insertion Loss

Insertion loss is a term commonly used to describe the performance of silencers for use in ducts and pipes. What we need to know about such devices is by how much they will reduce the amount of energy passing along a duct, and this is what an insertion loss tells us.

As one might expect, the method of measuring insertion loss is rather similar to the measurement of sound power level using an in-duct test. Two types of duct are generally required for duct silencers—static insertion loss and generated noise level.

In the static test, the silencer is placed near the centre of a long duct, with a sound source on one end, and an anechoic termination at the other (fig. 3.7(a)). With the source operating, the mean sound pressure level, L_1), is measured across a section of the duct some distance downstream of the silencer. The silencer is then removed, and replaced with the same length of plain duct. The average sound pressure level at the same measuring station is again determined, L_2, and the insertion loss of the silencer is defined as

$$\text{Static IL} = L_2 - L_1 \text{ dB} \qquad (3.12)$$

Insertion loss is normally given as the value in each of the standard octave bands (Table 1.5).

The test for generated noise level is necessary if the silencer is to be used in a duct carrying air or another gas. Under these conditions the flow through the silencer may well generate its own noise which will then propagate downstream. Obviously this flow generated sound energy will offset the full potential static insertion loss of the silencer. To be able to assess the nett performance of a duct silencer therefore, we must know both its static insertion loss, and the amount of noise it generates. An arrangement for doing this is shown in fig. 3.7 (b) which combines the static insertion loss duct with a reverberant room. On the upstream side of the test silencer, the static sound source is replaced by a fan, which provides a flow through the test silencer via a permanent silencer. Thus at

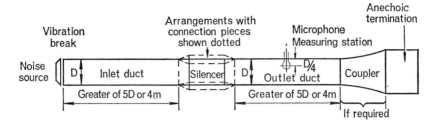

(a) Arrangement for measurement of static insertion loss

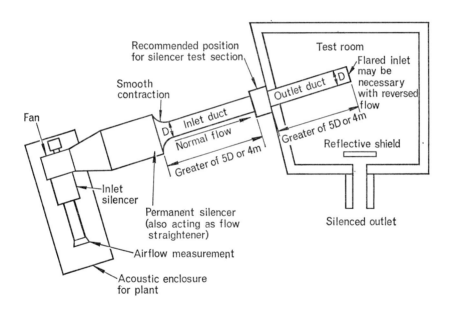

(b) Typical arrangement of installation for generated noise level measurement

Fig. 3.7. The measurement of duct silencer insertion loss (to BS 4718:1971)

the upstream side of the test silencer we have a "quiet" airflow. On the downstream side of the test silencer therefore, the only noise will be that generated by the flow itself—which of course is what we want to measure. From then on, we are simply measuring the sound power of this flow noise by a standard reverberant room method, and the sound power level is given by

E

$$PWL = SPL + 10 \log V - 10 \log T - 14 + X_r \quad dB \qquad (3.13)$$

where SPL is the average sound pressure level in the room at the stated
flow dB

V is the volume of the room m³

T is the reverberation time secs

X_r is the end reflection factor of the duct dB (see fig 5.7)

As an alternative, the duct could open into an anechoic chamber, and
the sound power level of the flow generated noise is then measured by a
free field traverse, as described earlier in this chapter.

The measurement of Absorption Coefficient

We have already mentioned absorption (equation 3.11), and will be
discussing it in more detail in the next chapter. To be able to evaluate
total absorption in a room, however, we must know the "absorption
coefficient", a, of the material of its internal surfaces. Quite simply, this
is defined as the ratio of the sound energy absorbed by a material, to the
total energy incident upon it. (We shall be discussing the mechanism by
which energy is absorbed in Chapter 6).

The two most common methods of measuring absorption coefficient are,
the standing wave tube method, and the reverberation room method.
Absorption coefficients are normally given as a curve of values of a plotted
at either the standard octave band or one-third octave band centre
frequencies (Table 1.5), or as tabulated values at particular frequencies.

Standing wave tube method

The basic element is a long rigid walled tube, closed at one end by a
heavy solid plug, and at the other by a sound source in the form of a
loudspeaker (fig. 3.8). Passing through the loudspeaker cone is a long
probe microphone mounted on a carriage, which moves along a graduated
scale.

The sample is placed against the plug and a pure tone sound is
generated by the loudspeaker. A plot of the variation of sound pressure
along the length of the tube, measured by moving the probe microphone on
its carriage, will show a series of maximum and minimum sound pressures.
The absorption coefficient of the material can be shown to be related to
the ratio of the sound pressure maximum, which occurs at the face of the
material, to the sound pressure minimum, which occurs one-quarter of the
wavelength away, by

$$a_0 = \frac{4}{n + 1/n + 2} \qquad (3.14)$$

where $n = p_{max}/p_{min}$.

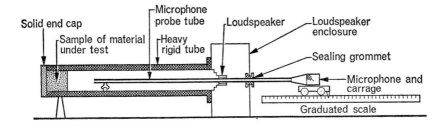

Fig. 3.8. Basic elements of standing wave tube for measurement of absorption coefficient

The suffix "o" after a denotes that this is a "normal incidence absorption coefficient". That is, the sample is absorbing sound which impinges upon it from the direction normal to the plane of its surface.

Reverberation room method

In a room, sound may impinge on an absorptive wall covering from any angle. In practical calculations of the behaviour of sound in rooms therefore, we need to know the "random incidence absorption coefficient" of the material. One can calculate this from the normal incidence values, but the method has its limitations. In any case, as explained in Chapter 4, we sometimes need to know the absorption characteristics of people and objects in a room, which obviously cannot be determined by the standing wave tube method.

The more general and useful method is simply to place a large sample of the material (at least 10 m²) in a reverberation room, and measure the reverberation time. The random incidence coefficient of the added material sample can be shown to be approximately

$$a = 0 \cdot 161 \, \frac{V}{S} \left(\frac{1}{T_1} - \frac{1}{T_2} \right) \tag{3.15}$$

where S is the area of the sample m²

V is the volume of the test room m³

T_1, T_2 are respectively the reverberation times with and without the sample in the room secs.

Note that for objects the quantity describing their absorptive characteristics is S.a (see Chapter 4).

The procedure for measuring absorption coefficient by the reverberant room method is given in British Standard 3638:1963.

CHAPTER 4

The calculation of noise levels

In Chapter 2, we learned that the quantity which is going to determine the effect of a noise on people is the sound pressure level produced in their vicinity. At some stage in the assessment of a particular problem we shall need to predict what that level will be.

Even if the problem already exists, and the offending sound levels can be determined by measurement, the noise control engineer will still have to specify what treatment is needed to control the noise. For this to be effective we must know on what parameters the sound pressure level depends in the particular circumstances. Only then can we decide which parameter must be changed and by how much. That is, only then can we design appropriate noise control measures.

The object of this chapter is to outline the more important calculations, and to show how they are derived.

With engineering assessments of noise, we are usually concerned with one of two types of problem, viz:

(i) Given the sound power level of a piece of industrial plant or other machinery, what will be the resultant sound pressure level at some specified point relative to it.

(ii) Knowing the sound pressure level at some specified point, what will be the sound pressure level at some other point, due to the same source.

The evaluation of (ii) sometimes means we first have to calculate the, as yet unknown, sound power level of the source. This is simply the reverse procedure of (i). More often, however, there is usually a direct relationship between the two sound pressure levels, as we shall see in the course of this chapter.

In all the calculations which follow, no mention is made specifically of frequency. Rather, it is implied that when we refer to sound power level, or sound pressure level, we mean the value at one frequency, or in one band of frequencies (octave or one-third octave). Obviously for a full assessment, the calculation must be repeated for all frequencies of interest.

The propagation of noise out-of-doors

The propagation of noise through a uniform still atmosphere is the simplest case we consider. Most practical problems in which the energy travels directly from source to observer, through the air, can be assessed from this model. Once we have calculated for the ideal, we can as we shall see later, make suitable corrections to take into account practical variations from the ideal, like weather conditions, and the presence of physical obstructions such as screens or barriers.

Unidirectional spherical propagation

In Chapter 1 we considered the case of a source radiating uniformly in all directions, suspended in the centre of a large space. By considering the value of acoustic intensity corresponding to the local sound pressure, (equation (1.6)), we concluded that if the sound pressure at distance r (in any direction) was p, the total acoustic power was given by

$$W = p^2/\rho c \cdot 4\pi r^2$$

we also have from equations (1.8) and (1.9) that

$$W = 10^{-12} \text{ antilog} \left(\frac{SWL}{10}\right) \text{ watts} \qquad (4.1)$$

$$p^2 = (2 \times 10^{-5})^2 \text{ antilog} \left(\frac{SPL}{10}\right) (N/m^2)^2 \qquad (4.2)$$

By substituting these into equation (1.6) and using consistent units we can relate sound pressure level to the source sound power level, by

$$SPL = SWL - 20 \log r - 11 \text{ dB} \qquad (4.3)$$

where SPL is the sound pressure level dB
    r is the distance of the receiving point from the source m
    SWL is the sound power level of the source dB re 10^{-12} watts.

EXAMPLE 4.1

A siren situated near the top of a tall building radiates 1 watt of acoustic power. Assuming this energy is radiated equally in all directions, calculate the sound pressure level 70 m from the siren.

From equation (1.9), Sound Power Level $= 10 \log \left(\dfrac{1}{10^{-12}}\right)$

$$= 120 \text{ dB}$$

From equation (4.3) $SPL = 120 - 20 \log (70) - 11$

$$= 72 \text{ dB}$$

It is clear from equation (4.3) that if the sound pressure level at one distance, say r_0, from the source is known, the sound pressure level at a greater distance r_1, can be calculated without first evaluating the sound power level of the source.

If the sound pressure level at r_0 is SPL_0
and the sound pressure level at r_1 is SPL_1

then $SPL_0 - SPL_1 = 20 \log r_1 - 20 \log r_0$

or $SPL_0 - SPL_1 = 20 \log \dfrac{r_1}{r_0} \text{ dB} \qquad (4.4)$

Equation (4.4) represents the well known inverse square law by which sound pressure level decreases by 6 dB per doubling of distance from the source. The physical explanation for this is quite easily seen if we refer back to our original model for spherical propagation (fig. 1.3). If we double the radius of the control sphere, then clearly, the same amount of energy from the source has to be spread over an area four times as large. Then the local acoustic intensity (energy per second per unit area) must be *decreased* by a factor of four, as must be the local acoustic (pressure)² (equation (1.3)). Whence from equation (1.8), sound pressure level must decrease by 6 dB.

Unidirectional hemispherical propagation

While the model of a noise source located in free space and radiating in all directions is representative of some practical situation (overflying aircraft, noise from the top of a tall building or industrial stack), by far the most common arrangement is when the source is near the ground. If the area around the source is again substantially free of reflecting surfaces or barriers, we have the important case of hemispherical propagation.

That is to say, all the energy that would have been radiated downwards had the source been in free space, is now reflected by the ground and constrained to radiate into the hemispherical region above the ground. By a principle similar to that of light images, the "downward" radiation pattern is superimposed upon the "upward" radiation pattern.

Now if we compare this situation with the simple model for spherical propagation shown in Fig. 1.3, we see that all the energy from the source has to pass through a control surface only half the area of the full sphere. This means of course that the local acoustic intensity at distance r from the source is doubled, whence from equation (1.8) the sound pressure level is increased by 3 dB.

Knowing then that for the same source sound power level, the sound pressure level at distance r from the source is increased by 3 dB, the relationship between SPL and SWL for hemispherical radiation follows directly from equation (4.3), i.e.

$$\text{SPL} = \text{SWL} - 20 \log r - 8 \text{ dB} \qquad (4.5)$$

EXAMPLE 4.2

If the siren referred to in example 4.1 is located at ground level, calculate the sound pressure level at 10 m.

As before   SWL $= 120$ dB

From equation (4.5), SPL $= 120 - 20 \log (10) - 8$
$$= 92 \text{ dB}$$

Directivity effects

As was pointed out in Chapter 3 not all sources radiate uniformly in all directions. If the source has marked directional characteristics, some factor must be added to the equation to account for directivity. Equations (4.3) and (4.5) give the sound pressure level at distance r metres from source in any direction. We can account for enhanced radiation in a particular direction by a simple decibel addition like the Directivity Index, DI, defined in equation (3.9).

Since
$$DI(\theta) = SPL(\theta) - SPL_{av} \text{ dB}$$
and since for unidirectional spherical radiation, from equation (4.3)
$$SPL_{av} = SWL - 20 \log r - 11$$
we have, for *directional* spherical radiation,
$$SPL(\theta) = SWL - 20 \log r + DI(\theta) - 11 \text{ dB} \quad (4.6)$$

It is obvious from the previous discussion that for unidirectional hemispherical radiation,
$$DI(\theta) = 3 \text{ dB} \quad (4.7)$$

Using this value, equation (4.6) reduces to equation (4.5) as previously derived.

EXAMPLE 4.3

When radiating into a spherical space, a small machine, known to generate a sound power level of 100 dB, produces a sound pressure level of 75 dB at an angle of 30° to its axis, and at a distance of 10 m.

Calculate the spherical directivity index at 30°, and the sound pressure level that will be produced at this angle 20 m from the machine when it is located at ground level.

From equation (4.3), $SPL_{av.} = 100 - 20 \log 10 - 11 \text{ dB}$
$$= 69 \text{ dB}$$
From equation (3.9), $DI(30°) = 75 - 69$
$$= 6 \text{ dB}$$

When the machine is at ground level, radiating into a hemispherical space, the spherical directivity index will be increased by 3 dB (equation (4.7)).

Hence from equation (4.6), $SPL = 100 - 20 \log (20) + (6 + 3) - 11 \text{ dB}$
$$= 72 \text{ dB}$$

Again, we may want to calculate the sound pressure level at some distance r_1 from the source, using a known sound pressure level nearer the source at distance say r_0.

If r_1 and r_0 are in the same angular direction relative to the source, then equation (4.4) applies directly, because the directivity will obviously be the same for both points.

If r_1 is in a different direction to r_0, we have to take into account any differences in directivity index, i.e.

if the directivity index in the direction of r_0 is $DI(0_0)$, and that in the direction of r_1 is $DI(\theta_1)$, then from equation (4.6)
$$SPL [r_0, \theta_0] = SWL - 20 \log r_0 + DI(\theta_0) - 11 \text{ dB}$$
and $SPL [r_1, \theta_1] = SWL - 20 \log r_1 + DI(\theta_1) - 11 \text{ dB}$

Subtracting
$$SPL [r_0, \theta_0] - SPL [r_1, \theta_1] = 20 \log\left(\frac{r_1}{r_0}\right) + DI(\theta_0) - DI(\theta_1) \text{ dB} \quad (4.8)$$

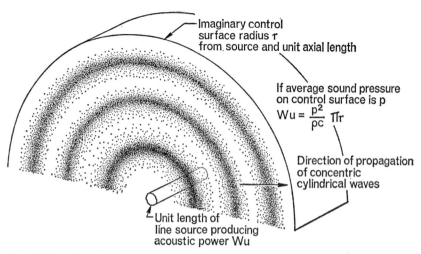

Fig. 4.1. Radiation from a line source

Propagation from a line source

Typical examples of a line source in noise control problems are a straight road with a uniform density of traffic along its length, or a straight pipe or duct radiating uniformly along its length. (The case of a duct radiating into a room is considered separately in Chapter 5).

The essential difference between a line source and a point source is that whereas the point source is free to radiate in all directions, the waves propagating from a line source form a series of concentric cylindrical surfaces, having their axis on the line of the source (see Fig. 4.1).

If we now think of the power radiated, not by the whole line source, but by unit length of it, W_u, it is clear that by the same argument we used to arrive at equation (1.6) for a spherically radiating source, the relationship between power per unit length of a line source at ground level and sound pressure distance r from the line, is

$$W_u = \frac{p^2}{\varrho c}.\pi r \qquad (4.9)$$

Note that "πr" is used rather than "$2\pi r$" since if the line source is located at ground level, the radiation must be into a semi-cylindrical space.

In terms of sound pressure level, using equations (4.1) and (4.2).

$$SPL = SWL_u - 10 \log r - 5 \text{ dB} \qquad (4.10)$$

where $SWL_u = 10 \log \dfrac{W_u}{10^{-12}}$ dB

W_u is the sound power per unit length radiated by the line source watts

r is the distance from the line source m.

Equation (4.10) shows an interesting feature of the noise from a line source. That is, the decay of sound pressure level with increasing distance from the line is only 3 dB per doubling of distance.

As with the point source, we can use this to predict the sound pressure level at some distance from the source, from a known sound pressure level at some reference distance.

If the sound pressure level at r_0 is SPL_0
and the sound pressure level at r_1 is SPL_1
then for the line source,

$$SPL_0 - SPL_1 = 10 \log \frac{r_1}{r_0} \text{ dB} \qquad (4.11)$$

When the line source has finite length, the situation becomes rather more complicated—the variation of sound pressure level with distance as represented by equation (4.10) applying only at points near the line, that is, for values of r less than about half the length of the source. For the purposes of engineering estimates, it can be assumed that the sound pressure level will decay by 3 dB per doubling of distance up to a distance of about half the length of the line source. For distances greater than about one length of the line source, assume a decay of 6 dB per doubling of distance.

Excess attenuation

All that has been said so far has applied to the radiation of sound in an idealised atmosphere. That is to say, one that is homogeneous, isotropic and completely free of reflecting surfaces. Even without the reflecting surfaces (the effect of which we shall examine later), air is normally anything but uniform throughout in its properties. The effect of these non-uniformities is generally to provide some degree of additional attenuation, over and above that due to the effect of distance alone. When calculating sound pressure level out of doors, due to a source of known sound power level, it is usual to first calculate the sound pressure level in the ideal conditions, using the foregoing equations, and then add the decibel corrections (positive or negative) due to the various atmospheric effects.

(a) *Molecular absorption*

The most important effect giving additional attenuation at large distances from the source is molecular absorption in the air. Because air has viscosity, some energy has to be used to overcome intermolecular friction. The result is that over long distances, a significant amount of energy can be removed from the sound waves. The orders of magnitude to be expected are shown in Fig. 4.2 in terms of decibels of extra attenuation for various frequencies as a function of distance from the source. These attenuations should be subtracted from the sound pressure level evaluated from the appropriate equation for ideal conditions.

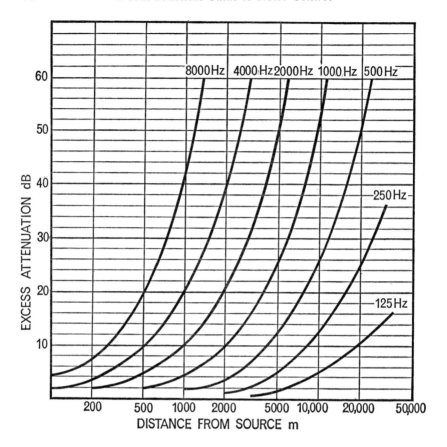

Fig. 4.2. Approximate additional attenuation due to air absorption

EXAMPLE 4.4

The noise radiated from the intake of a large process air supply fan located out of doors has the following octave band sound power level spectrum.

Octave Band Centre Freq.	Hz	63	125	250	500	1000	2000	4000	8000
Octave Band SWL	dB	88	97	110	108	102	96	90	85

Calculate the sound pressure level to be expected at a distance of 500 m from the fan, assuming the radiation is unidirectional.

Since the noise source is located at ground level, we take the case of hemispherical radiation.

From equation (4.5), $\text{SPL} = \text{SWL} - 20 \log (500) - 8 \text{ dB}$
$$= \text{SWL} - 62 \text{ dB}$$

In addition to the attenuation due to distance we have to take into account the attenuation due to air absorption, as indicated in the table below.

Octave Band Centre Freq.	Hz	63	125	250	500	1000	2000	4000	8000
SWL (given)	dB	88	97	110	108	102	96	90	85
Attenuation due to distance	dB	−62	−62	−62	−62	−62	−62	−62	−62
Air Absorption (Fig. 4.2)	dB	−0	−0	−0	−0	−2	−5	−9	−20
SPL at 500 m	dB	26	35	48	46	38	29	19	3

(b) *Wind and temperature gradients*

Wind and temperature gradients can have very peculiar effects. Sound travels faster in air as the temperature increases. The absolute speed also increases with wind speed (downwind propagation). This means that if wind speed increases with height, or we have a temperature inversion, the top regions of the sound waves travel faster, and the path the wave takes tends to be bent over, rather as shown in Fig. 4.3. The effect of a normal temperature gradient (decreasing with height) is much the same as that of upwind propagation. The effect of this phenomenon is to create a "shadow zone" just beyond the point where the lowest waves graze the ground, and then propagate upwards again. In the shadow zones the sound levels are usually less than they would be from normal propagation, because obviously some of the energy that would normally have been received there has been diffracted upwards.

With the temperature inversion and downwind propagation, the opposite happens. Energy which would normally have been radiated upwards is redirected downwards, in a sort of focussing effect on the ground. It is

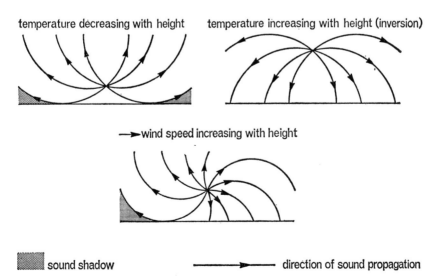

Fig. 4.3. Effect of meteorological conditions on sound propagation

possible through this effect to get a negative attenuation, that is, rather higher sound pressure levels than would be expected due to the distance and directivity alone.

Unfortunately, these effects of atmospheric conditions upon propagation are among the least quantified. So it is not possible to give general rules for taking them into account. As far as excess attenuation is concerned, in for example shadow zones, we have to regard this as a bonus to be added to our noise control measures, but not to be relied upon for design purposes. The worst case will be when we have any negative attenuation. In practice this will probably be small, not greater than 10 dB at frequencies upwards of 500 Hz and occur under conditions of marked temperature inversion and light winds. If these are likely to be at all prevalent in the area considered, it is wise to assume that the sound pressure level will be 5 to 10 dB higher than that due to distance alone, plus the appropriate molecular absorption allowance, for distances greater than about 250 m from the source.

(c) *Attenuation from screens and barriers*

So far we have considered only the effect of the properties of air over and above normal free field radiation. In most real environments however there are often buildings or similar objects which lie between the source and the observer and prevent line of sight between them. When a sound wave meets an obstacle like a fence or a building, a proportion of it is reflected, and the rest of the wave carries on past the edge of the obstacle.

However, the "bare" edge of a sound wave cannot sustain itself in free space—the vibrating air molecules at the end start themselves to act like sources and radiate in all directions. The result is that a sound wave which has passed the obstacle, bends, or diffracts round it into the shadow zone behind the obstacle.

Fig. 4.4 shows the attenuation in dB to be expected in these circumstances. Again, the attenuation should be subtracted from the sound pressure levels calculated for ideal radiation less any attenuation for molecular absorption.

EXAMPLE 4.5

Calculate the sound pressure level at 100 m from the fan described in Example 4.4, if a long brick wall 2 m high is placed between the fan and the observation point, at a distance of 2 m from the fan.

From the geometry of the arrangement, effective barrier height is 2 m, and angle into the sound shadow is approximately 46°.

With no barrier in position, the sound pressure level at 100 m from equation (4.5) is,

$$SPL = SWL - 20 \log (100) - 8 \text{ dB}$$
$$= SWL - 48 \text{ dB}$$

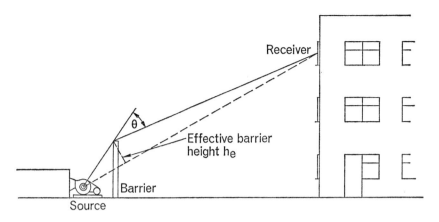

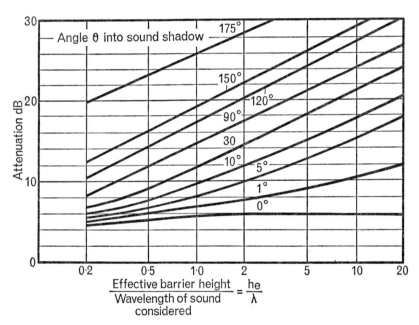

Fig. 4.4. Noise reduction due to a barrier

The sound pressure level taking into account the barrier effect is calculated as follows:

Octave band centre frequency Hz		63	125	250	500	1000	2000	4000	8000
(i) SWL (given)	dB	88	97	110	108	102	96	90	85
(ii) Attenuation due to distance	dB	−48	−48	−48	−48	−48	−48	−48	−48
(iii) SPL at 100 m without barrier	dB	40	49	62	60	54	48	42	37

continued

(iv) Wavelength (equation (1·2))	m	5·5	2·8	1·4	·70	·35	·17	·09	·04
(v) h_e/λ		·35	·70	1·4	2·8	5·7	11·8	22·5	50
(vi) Attenuation due to barrier (fig. 4.4 at 46°)	dB	−8	−11	−14	−18	−20	−22	−25	−29
(vii) SPL at 100 m with barrier ((iii) + (vi))	dB	32	38	48	42	34	26	17	8

One important point must be made here. That is, buildings and fences have finite width, which means that besides diffracting over the top, some energy will diffract round the sides. Besides evaluating attenuation due to the height of the obstacle therefore it is important to evaluate the attenuation due to the barrier effect of the width. The two sound pressure levels evaluated, one with attenuation due to vertical barrier and one with attenuation due to horizontal barrier, should then be added using Table 1.2.

The behaviour of sound in rooms

Sound levels in rooms of normal proportions

When discussing methods of measuring sound power levels in a room (Chapter 3), it was explained that by making the interior surfaces of the room suitably absorptive we could simulate an outdoor situation. If we stood at some point in the room we would receive only the energy from the source beamed directly at us. Because there was virtually no reflection from the surfaces of the rooms, we received none of the energy originally radiated in other directions. We then went on to see that if we made the surfaces fully reflective, we would obtain not only the direct sound energy, but in the steady state, all the other energy as well.

This is more representative of real rooms, although, except perhaps in some industrial situations, they are not usually fully reflective. What we need to know then is, given a machine of known sound power level in a room of known characteristics, how do we calculate the sound pressure at any point in the room. Fortunately life is made a little simpler for us by being able to consider the direct and reverberant (as energy is called after multiple reflection) energies separately.

The direct radiation we already know about. The energy intensity at distance r from the source is simply from equation (3.8)

$$\frac{p(\theta)^2}{\varrho c} = WQ_\theta/4\pi r^2$$

Now consider what happens to a sound wave on reflection. When the pressure wave reaches the wall it compresses the layer of air immediately next to the wall. Because the wall is much heavier, or more precisely, has a higher impedance than the air, the compressed boundary layer can only expand back towards the room interior, and so another acoustic wave is radiated, i.e. the main wave is reflected. In fact this statement is not quite accurate. Certainly the air can expand backward much more easily, and most of the incident energy is reflected. But there is some movement of the wall surface however heavy the material of the wall may be, and of course some of the incident energy must be used to move the surface. What happens to the energy that has passed into the wall need not concern us at the moment. The important point is that the reflected energy is something less than incident energy. How much less?

A measure of the amount of energy absorbed by a surface is its absorption coefficient. This is the ratio of the energy absorbed by a surface, to the energy incident upon it. It is usually denoted by α and expressed as a decimal fraction or as a percentage. Absorption coefficients are not easily calculated, but they are easily measured as explained in Chapter 3 and values are widely published for most building materials. (See Appendix A.)

Turning back then to our reflected wave, the energy in it must be a factor of $(1-\bar{\alpha})$ less than the energy in the incident wave, because by definition $\bar{\alpha}$ of the energy has been absorbed. The bar over α here denotes an average absorption coefficient for the whole room. Statistically, this will be the effective value after many reflections even if the various surfaces have different absorption coefficients.

The value of the average absorption coefficient can be calculated quite simply. If we have an area S_1 of material in the room having an absorption coefficient α_1, an area S_2 with absorption coefficient α_2, and so on, the average absorption coefficient is given by

$$\bar{\alpha} = \frac{S_1\alpha_1 + S_2\alpha_2 + S_3\alpha_3 + \ldots \text{etc.}}{S} \tag{4.12}$$

where S is the total surface area of the room

Note that objects in the room like furniture, theatre seats, even people, contribute towards the absorption coefficient. Values of S.α for such items are known (see Appendix A) and should be added to the numerator of equation (4.12). The quantity S.α is known as the "absorption" of an area of surface or an object and is usually expressed in m^2 units.

EXAMPLE 4.6

A general office measure 10 m $\times$ 16 m $\times$ 4 m high. Windows in one of the large walls occupy an area measuring 15 m $\times$ 2 m, and in each of the smaller walls 9 m $\times$ 2 m. The remaining wall area is plaster finish. The ceiling is covered with 25 mm thick absorptive tiles, and the floor covering is 6 mm thin pile carpeting. When occupied the room will contain 20 people seated at wooden office-type desks.

Calculate the average absorption coefficient in the empty room, and when it is occupied.

Absorption coefficients for the various room surfaces may be taken as follows (see also appendix A):

Frequency	Hz	63	125	250	500	1000	2000	4000	8000
Ceiling 160 m²		·05	·10	·35	·70	·75	·65	·50	·50
Walls (less windows) 142 m²		·04	·04	·05	·06	·08	·04	·06	·05
Windows 66 m²		·08	·15	·06	·04	·03	·02	·02	·02
Floor 160 m²		·05	·05	·05	·10	·20	·45	·65	·65
Desk and chair (value of S.α each—m² units)		·02	·03	·05	·05	·10	·15	·10	·10
People (value of S.α each—m² units)		·30	·40	·75	1·10	1·30	1·40	1·10	1·10

To obtain the average absorption coefficient, it is first necessary to calculate the total value of S.α in the room at each frequency, as follows:

Frequency		Hz	63	125	250	500	1000	2000	4000	8000
(i) Ceiling	m² units		8	16	56	112	120	104	80	80
(ii) Walls	m² units		6	6	7	9	11	6	9	7
(iii) Windows	m² units		5	10	4	3	2	1	1	1
(iv) Floor	m² units		8	8	8	16	32	72	104	104
(v) Total absorption—empty room m² units			27	40	75	140	165	183	194	192
(vi) 20 desks and chairs m² units			0	1	1	1	2	3	2	2
(vii) 20 people m² units			6	8	15	22	26	28	22	22
(viii) Total absorption—occupied room m² units			33	49	91	163	193	214	218	216

Room surface area = 528 m²

Average Absorption Coefficient from equation (4.12)

			63	125	250	500	1000	2000	4000	8000
(ix) Empty room (v/528)			·05	·08	·14	·27	·31	·35	·37	·36
(x) Occupied room (viii/528)			·06	·09	·17	·31	·37	·40	·41	·41

To return to the question of how much energy remains in the sound wave after reflection, it is clear that, taking the room as a whole, the proportion of the total power supplied (the sound power of the source W) which goes to make up the reverberant energy in the room is

$$W_{REV} = W(1 - \bar{\alpha}) \tag{4.13}$$

This supply to the reverberant field, is of course a continuous process. In the steady state it must be equal to the rate at which energy is absorbed by the room boundaries, which is the next thing we have to calculate.

We have already referred in passing to "energy density" (Chapter 3—reverberant room testing). Just as we could relate the *rate* at which sound energy is transmitted through unit area perpendicular to the direction of wave propagation—or, acoustic intensity—to the local sound pressure (equation (1.3)), so we can show that the *amount* of energy contained in unit volume of the medium—or energy density—is related to the local sound pressure by

$$D = p^2/\varrho c^2 \tag{4.14}$$

Since by definition the energy density in a diffuse field is nearly constant, the average level of reverberant energy throughout the room will be

$$D.V = \frac{p^2}{\varrho c^2}.V$$

where V is the volume of the room.

Each time reflection occurs therefore, statistically a quantity $\bar{\alpha}.V.p^2/\varrho c^2$ of energy will be extracted. If we can calculate the number of times this will occur in one second, we know how much power is being extracted from the room.

Here we have to introduce the concept of "mean free path" of a particular wave. This has been studied experimentally, and again statistically it can be shown that the average distance travelled by a particular wave between successive reflections is 4V/S, where V is the volume of the room, and S is the total surface area of all reflecting surfaces. Then the time for a wave to travel one mean free path is obviously 4V/cS where c is the velocity of sound, and the number of mean free paths travelled in one second, i.e. the number of reflections occurring in one second, is cS/4V.

Then the total energy removed from the room in one second is

$$\frac{cS}{4V}.\bar{\alpha}V.\frac{p^2}{\varrho c^2}$$

Since this must be equal to the power being fed into the reverberant field W_{REV} we obtain using equation (4.13)

$$\frac{p^2}{\varrho c} = 4W.\frac{(1 - \bar{\alpha})}{S.\bar{\alpha}} \tag{4.15}$$

The quantity $(1 - \bar{\alpha})/S.\bar{\alpha}$ is called the "room constant" and is normally denoted by R_c. Equation (4.15) represents the "reverberant" energy intensity which will be roughly independent of position within the room. We have already seen (from equation (3.8)) that the direct energy intensity is given by

$$\frac{p^2}{\varrho c} = W\frac{Q_\theta}{4\pi r^2} \tag{4.16}$$

If we now add the direct and reverberant energy intensities, equations (4.15) and (4.16), we get the total energy intensity, i.e.

$$p^2/\varrho c = W\left[\frac{Q_\theta}{4\pi r^2} + \frac{4}{R_c}\right]$$

Or, by adding the relevant reference quantities (equations (4.1) and (4.2)) to both sides and choosing consistent units, we can express the whole thing in terms of decibels, i.e.

$$SPL = SWL + 10\log\left[\frac{Q_\theta}{4\pi r^2} + \frac{4}{R_c}\right] dB \tag{4.17}$$

F

where r is the distance from the source m

   Q_θ is the directivity factor of the source in the direction of r

   R_c is the room constant $S\bar{\alpha}/(1 - \bar{\alpha})$ m² units

   S is the surface area of the room m²

   $\bar{\alpha}$ is the average absorption coefficient in the room (from equation (4.12)).

The value of Q_θ depends upon the acoustic characteristics of the particular source being considered, and also upon its position relative to the room surfaces. Details of the directional characteristics of a particular source, say a piece of office equipment, or mechanical services plant, usually has to be obtained from the manufacturer's data or from previous tests. The effect of the position of the source relative to the room surfaces is discussed in detail in relation to ventilation grilles in Chapter 5. In the context of the present discussion, and in the absence of detailed knowledge of the particular source characteristics it is usually sufficiently accurate to assume a unidirectional source and take the values of Q_θ shown in Table 4.1.

TABLE 4.1

Values of Directivity Factor and Directivity Index for a unidirectional source located in a large room (see also fig. 5.9)

Position of source	*Directivity Factor* Q_θ	*Directivity Index* DI dB
Near centre of room	1	0
At centre of wall, floor or ceiling	2	3
Centre of edge formed by junction of two adjacent surfaces	4	6
Corner formed by junction of three adjacent surfaces	8	9

EXAMPLE 4.7

It is proposed to install a data processing unit in the office described in Example 4.6. The unit incorporates a cooling fan which may be assumed to be the dominant noise source. The sound power level of the fan is known from manufacturers' data (see table below) and it may be assumed that the radiation pattern is unidirectional. In the installed position the unit will be near the centre of the large unglazed wall, and the fan will be approximately 2 m from the floor. Calculate the sound pressure level to be expected 3 m from the unit.

The direct radiation term in equation (4.17) will be independent of frequency, and can be evaluated first. Since the source is effectively near the centre of one wall, $Q_\theta = 2$, from table 4.1. Hence

$$Q_\theta/4\pi r^2 = 2/4\,\pi\,(3)^2$$
$$= 1\cdot77 \times 10^{-2}\ \text{m}^{-2}$$

The rest of the calculation is best tabulated as follows:

Octave Band Centre Freq. Hz	63	125	250	500	1000	2000	4000	8000
(i) SWL (given) dB	40	45	50	53	54	51	46	40
(ii) $\bar{\alpha}$ (from example 4.6—								
line (x))	·06	·09	·17	·31	·37	·40	·41	·41
(iii) $R_c = S\bar{\alpha}/(1 - \bar{\alpha})$								
(S = 528 m²) m² units	35·6	53·8	119·5	236·0	306·5	356·5	369·5	366·0
(iv) $4/R_c \times 10^2$ m⁻²	11·39	7·44	3·35	1·70	1·31	1·12	1·08	1·09
(v) $(1·77 \times 10^{-2} + 4/R) \times$								
10^2 m⁻²	13·16	9·21	5·12	3·47	3·08	2·89	2·85	2·86
(vi) $10 \log ((v) \times 10^{-2})$ dB	−9	−10	−13	−15	−15	−15	−15	−15
Sound pressure level at 3 m								
((i) +(vi)) dB	31	35	37	38	39	36	31	25

Equation (4.17) shows an interesting characteristic of the sound field in a room. For a given room constant R_c, there will obviously be a distance r from the source where the quantity representing the direct energy, $Q_0/4\pi r^2$, starts to dominate the quantity representing the reverberant energy, $4/R_c$. We can think of this as a sort of "critical" distance. Between this point and the source, because the direct field is dominant, the sound level is the same as it would be if the source were in a completely free field. In other words the room is having virtually no effect, and equation (4.6) applies.

On the other hand, beyond the critical point, the sound field is entirely reverberant. The distance from the source r, does not come into this part of the equation, and the level is everywhere constant.

The net result is that if one were to plot the variation of sound pressure level with increasing distance from the source, one would find that up to the critical distance, the sound pressure level would follow the inverse square law as in the case of free field radiation. Beyond this point, instead of continuing to decrease, the sound pressure level evens out to remain virtually constant throughout the remainder of the room.

How far exactly the critical point is from the source clearly depends upon the relative magnitudes of the two terms in the bracket (equation (4.17)). For acoustically "hard" rooms, the value of the average absorption coefficient and hence the room constant will be low. Then the reverberant field will dominate up to relatively short distances from the source.

The reverse will occur when the room is highly absorptive and the value of the room constant is large. Figure 4.5 gives an indication of the relative importance of the reverberant and direct fields, for various acoustic conditions of rooms, characterised by the value of their room constant.

Note that the solution tabulated in Example 4.7 can be obtained directly from fig. 4.5. Enter the chart at 3 m (horizontal scale). Where this line intersects the Q = 2 curve at the appropriate value of R_c (line (iii) in the example), the decibel correction to convert SWL to SPL at the particular frequency can be read off on the vertical scale.

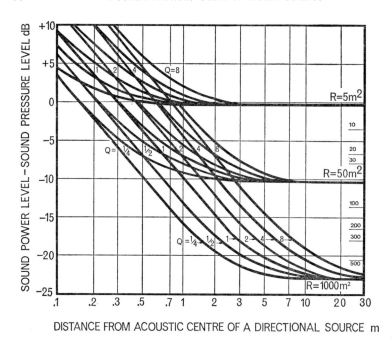

DISTANCE FROM ACOUSTIC CENTRE OF A DIRECTIONAL SOURCE m

Fig. 4.5. Variation of sound pressure level with distance from source

Sound levels in "open plan" offices

A particular problem arises in Burolandschaft, or so called open plan offices. A feature of these is that the width and length are very much greater than the height. Not a very significant point it may be thought, but consider for a moment on what basis we arrived at the general expression for the sound pressure level in a room, equation (4.17). The whole argument rested on the assumption that outside the direct field, in the reverberant field, the sound energy was diffuse—that is to say there was a fairly constant level throughout the room. And how did this arise? Because the interior surfaces, walls, floor and ceilings were all contributing together to provide the multiple reflection of the sound waves, which is essential for complete diffusion.

If we now "remove" the walls by making them much further away from the source than the ceiling and the floor, and moreover, make the ceiling and floor reasonably absorptive, we alter the acoustic conditions drastically. The behaviour of sound in such rooms is rather complicated and still not yet fully explained. One thing is generally agreed however, and that is that the reverberant field as we have come to understand it, does not exist. What does happen is that up to a certain distance from the source the sound pressure falls off as it would for a point source in free field conditions, that is at 6 dB per doubling of distance. Beyond this the rate of decay is only about 3 dB per doubling of distance. At some further point the decay again increases to 6 dB per doubling of distance (Fig. 4.6).

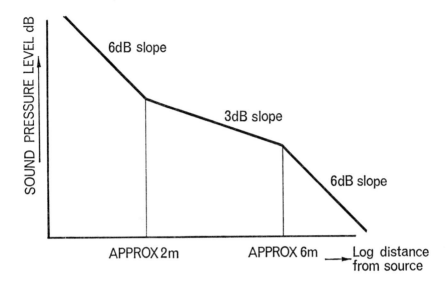

Fig. 4.6. Variation of sound pressure level in open plan offices

One explanation which has been proposed for this behaviour is based on the theory of acoustic images. Acoustic images behave rather like light images. That is, we can replace a first reflected wave reaching an observer, by the direct wave radiated by an imaginary source situated on the other side of the reflecting surface as a "mirror" image of the real source. The second reflected wave can be replaced by the direct wave from a second image, and so on (Fig. 4.7). Unfortunately things get very complicated as far as calculation is concerned, because we have to reduce the strength of each image source to compensate for the amount of energy that will have been removed from the real reflected wave by the absorptive properties of the ceiling and the floor.

We might then explain the observed behaviour in the following terms. Close to the source, the strength of even the first reflected wave is much less than the direct sound, because of the high absorption usually provided by the floor and ceiling finishes. In other words the radiation we get from the real source is very much stronger than that from the first image. This means that at first, as one moves away from the source, the direct radiation dominates—hence the 6 dB decay per doubling of distance. This decay continues however only until the direct sound becomes comparable with the sum of the first, second, third etc. reflected waves. Now

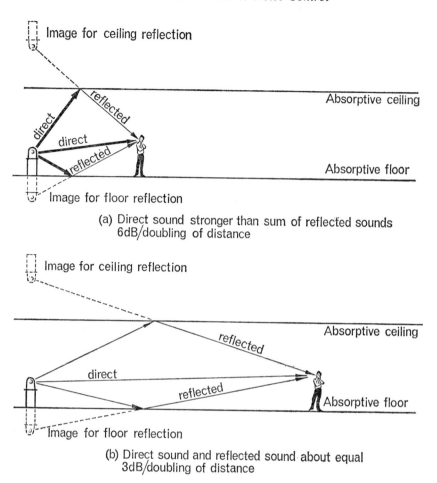

(a) Direct sound stronger than sum of reflected sounds
6dB/doubling of distance

(b) Direct sound and reflected sound about equal
3dB/doubling of distance

Fig. 4.7. Behaviour of sound in open plan office

the reflected waves start appearing to be stronger. At this point the source appears more like a line source, consisting of the point source and its first few images. Hence, as equation (4.11) shows we are now in a region where sound pressure level falls off only by 3 dB for each doubling of distance. Eventually we get far enough from the "line" source to see its "ends"—for although in theory there are an infinite number of image sources, their diminishing strength means that only the first few are really contributing, particularly at some distance from the real source.

The situation becomes even more complicated when we have to take into account the presence of furniture and equipment which may be highly reflective. As far as calculation is concerned, the key is the estimation of the distance at which the decay rate changes, first from 6 dB to 3 dB and then back to 6 dB per doubling of distance. As a guide, the first change appears to take place at a distance of about 2m from the source, and the second about 6m, for room proportions used in current design practice.

This means that if we have a point source, say an office machine, of known SWL, then up to 2 metres from the source the sound pressure level may be estimated as for free field conditions (equation (4.6)) i.e.

$$SPL = SWL - 20 \log r + DI(\theta) - 11 \text{ dB}$$

where r is the distance from the source in metres, and is not greater than 2m.

Beyond 2 metres, we may estimate the sound pressure level using the relationship for a line source, equation (4.11), and reduce the sound pressure level at 2m by 3 dB for each doubling of distance.

For distances greater than 6m, we then revert back to reducing the sound pressure level by 6 dB for each doubling of distance.

Sound transmission through partitions

Room to room calculations

Up to now we have been considering the problem of calculating noise levels when source and observer are in the same "space"—that is either out-of-doors or in the same room. We turn now to another important class of problem, where the source and the observer are in adjacent rooms, separated by some impervious barrier which completely separates them (as opposed to a screen which allows sound energy to diffract over the top or round the edges). In practice such barriers would be formed by walls, ceilings, floors (if one room is above the other) or the panels of a special enclosure made for the source. For convenience all such barriers are referred to as "partitions".

We can state the problem as follows. Given the situation of two adjacent rooms of known construction and interior finish, one of which contains a source of known sound power level, and the other a receiver, what will be the reverberant sound pressure level in the receiving room?

The first stage is to calculate the sound pressure level which will exist near the source side of the partition separating the two rooms. This is usually a straightforward matter of applying equation (4.17). Alternatively, if the source and the room containing it are already in operation, the average sound pressure near the partition can be measured directly.

Now we have to calculate how the sound energy is affected in its passage from source to receiver through the partition. We saw in the discussion on reverberant sound fields that when a sound wave met an impervious barrier like a partition, part of its energy was reflected, and part was used to move the surface of the partition. In that case we were concerned only with the energy that was reflected. Here we are concerned with the energy which passes into the partition.

Now what happens to that energy? First it has physically to move the partition, either as a solid panel, or just the top layer—depending on the construction and on the frequency of the sound. In either case work will obviously have to be done to overcome the partition's own resistance to movement, so some of the energy will be lost that way. The rest of it will be used to compress the layer of air immediately next to the surface on the other side of the partition. In other words, recalling our first piston-in-tube model of an acoustic source, the rest of the energy is radiated as sound on the other side.

What we are interested in for the purpose of calculating the eventual sound pressure level in the receiving room, is the net amount of energy passed through. We would expect this to depend obviously upon the construction of the partition, and so we need a parameter which, for a given construction, tells us what proportion of the incident energy reappears as sound energy on the other side. This parameter we call the "sound transmission coefficient" normally denoted by τ, and defined as the ratio of the energy transmitted through a partition, to the energy incident upon it. In fact, because we are used to working with decibels, we think in terms, not so much of the transmission coefficient as the "sound reduction index", R, which was defined in equation (3.10) by

$$R = 10 \log_{10} (1/\tau) \text{ dB}$$

Now although R by definition is the difference in sound power on either side of the partition, this is not the same as saying that R is simply the difference between sound pressure level on either side. In the first place, for a given pressure on the source side, and for a given partition construction, the sound pressure level on the other side is dependent entirely upon the acoustic characteristics of the receiving room.

As we have already learned in the discussion leading to equation (4.15), for a given amount of sound power passing into the receiving room, the higher the average absorption coefficient in that room, the lower will be the energy density, and hence reverberant sound pressure level. We must therefore take into account in the calculation some measure of the absorptive characteristics of the receiving room.

Another obvious factor which must be taken into account is the size of the partition—for a given construction a large area partition will allow more of the total energy to pass through than one of small area. Hence sound energy density in the receiving room will be higher, as in turn must be the reverberant sound pressure level.

The final equation we use stems directly from equation (3.11) which we rewrite to give the reverberant sound pressure level in the receiving room, i.e.

$$SPL_2 = SPL_1 - R + 10 \log S_p - 10 \log A \text{ dB} \qquad (4.18)$$

where SPL_2 is the reverberant sound pressure level in the receiving room, dB

SPL_1 is the average sound pressure level on the source side of the partition, dB

R is the sound reduction index of the partition, dB

S_p is the area of the partition, m²

A is the total absorption ($= S.\bar{\alpha}$) in the receiving room, m² units

S is the surface area in the receiving room, m²

$\bar{\alpha}$ is the average absorption coefficient in the receiving room (from equation (4.12)).

It will be noted that in equation (4.18) we use as a measure of the absorptive properties of the receiving room the quantity $S.\bar{\alpha}$. Whereas in the calculation of sound pressure level in the same room as the source, we used the room constant $S.\bar{\alpha}/(1-\bar{\alpha})$. Providing the average absorption coefficient is not greater than about 0·3 (which is the case for all but the most acoustically "dead" rooms), the difference between the two will amount to only a decibel or so in the final result. The room constant has more general use, but for most engineering applications $S.\bar{\alpha}$ will suffice. (Room constant R_c also has the unfortunate possibility of being confused with sound reduction index R).

EXAMPLE 4.8

The room adjacent to the office described in Example 4.6 is to be used as a factory machine shop, the large unglazed wall forming the partition between the two rooms. On the machine shop side of the wall, it is estimated that the sound pressure levels will reach the values given in the table below. If the reverberant sound pressure level in the office, due to the operation of the machine shop, is not to exceed NC 40, calculate the required sound reduction index for the dividing wall.

Octave Band Centre Freq. Hz		63	125	250	500	1000	2000	4000	8000
(i) SPL₁ (machine shop side—given)	dB	78	82	85	89	90	87	87	80
(ii) SPL₂ (NC40—fig. 2.8)	dB	66	57	50	46	41	39	38	36
(iii) 10 log Sp (Sp = 16 m × 4 m)	dB	18	18	18	18	18	18	18	18
(iv) 10 log A (A = line (viii) example 4.6)	dB	15	17	20	22	23	23	23	23
(v) From equation (4.18) R = (i) − (ii) + (iii) − (iv)	dB	15	26	33	39	44	43	44	39

Average sound reduction index

It has been implied in the discussion so far that the partition referred to has been of uniform construction throughout. This is not, of course, always the case. Many walls between rooms require an access door, many have windows or service holes, all of which constitute acoustically "weak" areas. When this happens, one cannot use in any of the foregoing equations simply the sound reduction index of the main structure. As we shall see in the chapter on noise control, quite serious errors can result if one does this.

To take account of weak areas in a main structure, one must use a value of sound reduction index averaged over the whole partition.

In the same way as we defined sound reduction index in equation (3.10), the average value is defined by:

$$R_{av} = 10 \log (1/\tau_{av}) \text{ dB} \qquad (4.19)$$

where τ_{av} is the average transmission coefficient.

This will be determined not only by the individual transmission coefficients of the various components of the partition, but also by their areas. If we had for example a masonry wall containing a window, a door, and a hole for services between the two rooms, the average transmission coefficient would be calculated from:

$$\tau_{av} = \frac{\tau_m S_m + \tau_w S_w + \tau_d S_d + \tau_h S_h + \ldots \text{etc.}}{S_p}$$

$$(4.20)$$

where S_p is the total area of the partition m²

$\tau_m, \tau_w, \tau_d, \tau_h$, etc. are the transmission coefficients of respectively, masonry, window, door, hole and any other discontinuity of surface.

S_m, S_w, S_d, S_h, etc. are the areas of those surfaces m².

The value of R_{av} evaluated from equations (4.19) and (4.20) should always be used in equation (4.18) if the partition is not of uniform construction.

EXAMPLE 4.9

To achieve the required sound reduction index of the dividing wall referred to in Example 4.8 it is proposed to use a 112 mm thick brick construction. The wall will include a window of area 1 m × 2 m, constructed of two panes of 6 mm glass in separate frames on either side of the wall. If a communicating door of area 2 m × 2 m is to be included, calculate the required sound reduction index of the door.

Octave Band Centre Freq. Hz		63	125	250	500	1000	2000	4000	8000
(i) Required R_{av} (example 4.8—line (v))	dB	15	26	33	39	44	43	44	39
(ii) τ_{av} (Equation 4.19) × 10³			31·6	2·5	·50	·126	·04	·05	·04	·126
(iii) τ_{av} Sp (Sp = 16 m × 4 m) × 10³	m²	2025	160	32	8·1	2·6	3·2	2·6	8·1
(iv) Rm (Appendix B)	dB	30	36	37	40	46	54	57	59
(v) τ_m (equation 3.10) × 10³			1·0	·25	·20	·10	·025	·004	·002	·0013
(vi) $\tau_m S_m$ (S_m = 64 m² − (4m² + 2m²)) × 10³ m²		58	14·5	11·6	5·8	1·45	·23	·12	·008

(vii) Rw (Appendix B)	dB	20	28	30	38	45	49	53	50
(viii) τ_w (equation (3.10)) $\times\ 10^3$		10	1·6	1·0	·16	·032	·013	·005	·01
(ix) $\tau_w\ S_w$ (S_w = 1 m $\times$ 2 m) $\times\ 10^3$	m²	20	3·2	2·0	·32	·064	·026	·01	·02
(x) $\tau_d\ S_d$ = (i) − ((vi) + (ix)) (Eqn. (4.20)) $\times\ 10^3$	m²	1947	142·3	18·4	1·98	1·086	2·994	2·47	8·072
(xi) τ_d (S_a = 2 m $\times$ 2 m) $\times\ 10^3$		487	35·6	4·6	·495	·272	·749	·62	2·02
(xii) R_d = 10 log ($1/\tau_d$ $\times\ 10^{-3}$) (equation (3·10))	dB	3	15	23	33	36	31	32	27

This will require either two normal doors arranged with a short tunnel to form a sound lock, or a specially constructed steel "acoustic" door (see chapter 7).

Transmission from inside to outside

One type of problem we are sometimes faced with, is the calculation of the level outside a building or enclosure containing a noisy machine or process.

First we have to know the sound pressure level just inside the walls. As before equation (4.17) can be used directly to calculate this.

Equation (4.18) however, cannot be used to predict the levels outside since it applies only to the reverberant level in the receiving space. Instead we use the following:

$$SPL_2 = SPL_1 - R - 6 \text{ dB} \qquad (4.21)$$

where SPL_2 is the sound pressure level immediately outside the partition dB

SPL_1 is the sound pressure level next to the partition on the source side, dB

R is the sound reduction index of the partition structure immediately next to the receiving point, dB.

As we move further away from the wall, the relationship becomes rather more complicated. We have to start taking into account not only the area of the partition which is radiating, but also its shape and proportions, both of which determine the directivity of its radiation pattern. For engineering purposes however, an estimate is often sufficient and for distances greater than about one wall width from the partition this can be obtained from:

$$SPL_2 = SPL_1 - R_{av} + 10 \log S_p - 20 \log r - 14 \text{ dB} \qquad (4.22)$$

where S_p is the area of the wall m²

r is the distance from the wall m

R_{av} is the average sound reduction index for the complete wall dB (equation (4.19) and (4.20)).

EXAMPLE 4.10

The outside wall of a boiler room faces the windows of an apartment building, the distance between the two buildings being 20 m. The boiler room wall is constructed of 112 mm thick brickwork and measures 6 m × 4 m high. A fresh air inlet louvre is necessary in the boiler room wall of overall area 2 m × 1 m, and this will be a sound attenuating louvre of proprietary manufacture (see chapter 7). Given the manufacturers performance data shown in the table below, calculate the maximum sound pressure level that can be permitted inside the boiler room, if (a) the sound pressure level on a pedestrian concourse just outside the wall is not to exceed NR 45, (b) the sound pressure level just outside the apartment windows is not to exceed NR 35.

Octave Band Centre Freq.	Hz	63	125	250	500	1000	2000	4000	8000
(a) *SPL immediately opposite louvre*									
(i) SPL_1 (NR45, fig. 2.9)	dB	70	60	54	49	45	42	40	39
(ii) R_{louvre} (manufacturers data)	dB	5	7	10	13	18	21	15	13
(iii) SPL in boiler room = (i) + (ii) + 6 (eqn. 4.21)	dB	81	73	70	68	69	69	61	58
(b) *SPL at apartment windows*									
(iv) R_{wall} (Appendix B)	dB	30	36	37	40	46	54	57	59
(v) τ_{wall} (Eqn. (3.10)) $\times 10^3$		1·0	·25	·20	·10	·025	·004	·002	·0013
(vi) $\tau_{wall} S_{wall}$ (S_{wall} = 24 m² − 2 m²) $\times 10^3$	m²	22	5·5	4·4	2·2	·55	·088	·044	·029
(vii) τ_{louvre} (Eqn. (3.10) and line (ii)) $\times 10^3$		320	200	100	50	16	8	32	50
(viii) $\tau_{louvre} S_{louvre}$ (S_{louvre} = 1 m × 2 m) $\times 10^3$	m²	640	400	200	100	32	16	64	100
(ix) $\tau_{av} S_p$ = (vi) + (viii) (Eqn. (4.20)) $\times 10^3$	m²	662	406	204	102	32·6	16·1	64	100
(x) τ_{av} (S_p = 6 m × 4 m) $\times 10^3$		27·6	16·9	8·5	4·25	1·36	·67	2·67	4·17
(xi) R_{av} (Eqn. (4.19))	dB	16	18	21	24	29	32	26	24
(xii) SPL_2 (NR35, fig. 2.9)	dB	62	52	45	39	35	32	30	29
(xiii) 10 log S_p (S_p = 6 m × 4 m)	dB	14	14	14	14	14	14	14	14
(xiv) 20 log r (r = 20 m)	dB	26	26	26	26	26	26	26	26
(xv) SPL in boiler room ((xii) + (xi) − (xiii) + (xiv) + 14)	dB	104	96	92	89	90	90	82	79

Comparison of lines (iii) and (xv) shows that the limit on boiler room noise will be set by the criterion of NR 45 immediately outside the fresh air louvre.

Noise reduction due to enclosure

Frequently one finds that the only way of reducing noise levels in a room caused by a machine or a piece of equipment in the same room, is to completely enclose the machine. The problem then is to predict by how much the reverberant noise level in the room will be reduced, or alternatively, for a specified noise level reduction required, what value of sound reduction index will be required for the walls of the enclosure.

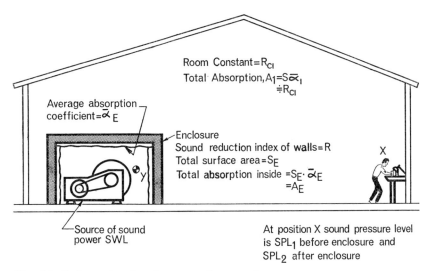

Room Constant=R_{cl}
Total Absorption,$A_1=S\bar{\alpha}_1$
$\doteqdot R_{cl}$

Average absorption coefficient=$\bar{\alpha}_E$

Enclosure
Sound reduction index of walls=R
Total surface area=S_E
Total absorption inside =$S_E \cdot \bar{\alpha}_E$
$=A_E$

X

Source of sound power SWL

At position X sound pressure level is SPL_1 before enclosure and SPL_2 after enclosure

Fig. 4.8. Noise reduction due to enclosure of source

The situation is shown diagrammatically in fig. 4.8. First the reverberant level in the room say at position X before enclosure, is, from equation (4.17).

$$SPL_1 = SWL + 10 \log \left(\frac{4}{R_{cl}}\right) dB \qquad (4.23)$$

where SPL_1 is the reverberant sound pressure level at position X before enclosure, dB

SWL is the sound power level of the source, dB

R_{cl} is the room constant, m² units.

When the enclosure is fitted, the new sound pressure level at position X can be estimated from the sound pressure level which now exists just inside the wall of the enclosure (position Y), directly from equation (4.18) i.e.

$$SPL_2 = SPL_Y - R + 10 \log S_E - 10 \log A_1 \qquad (4.24)$$

where SPL_2 is the sound pressure level at position X after enclosure, dB
SPL_Y is the sound pressure level just inside the wall of the enclosure (position Y), dB
R is the sound reduction index of the enclosure walls, dB
S_E is the total surface area of the enclosure, m²
A_1 is the absorption of the room ($= S_1\bar{\alpha_1}$) m² units
S_1 is the total surface area of the room, m²
$\bar{\alpha_1}$ is the average absorption coefficient in the room (equation (4.12)).

To get the reduction in reverberant sound pressure level in the room, we subtract equation (4.24) from equation (4.23) giving

$$SPL_1 - SPL_2 = SWL - SPL_Y + R - 10 \log S_E +$$
$$10 \log \frac{4}{R_{cl}} + 10 \log A_1 \text{ dB} \qquad (4.25)$$

Considering the last two terms, provided the average absorption coefficient is not greater than about 0·3 which is true for most factory and office spaces, we will not incur any great error by assuming R_{cl} the room constant, and A_1 the absorption, are the same, then

$$10 \log \frac{4}{R_{cl}} + 10 \log A_1 = 10 \log 4 \text{ dB} \qquad (4.26)$$

We can replace the term (SWL–SPL_Y) using equation (4.17) directly, by considering the inside of the enclosure to be a separate room and considering SPL_Y to be the reverberant sound pressure level. This is obviously an oversimplification since enclosures are often designed to fit closely to the surfaces of the offending machines, and a diffuse reverberant field as understood in earlier discussions probably does not exist. On the other hand, providing there is no mechanical excitation of the enclosure walls (see "noise control"), the error is not likely to be large in practice. On that understanding, we can obtain directly from equation (4.17).

$$SWL - SPL_Y = -10 \log \frac{4}{R_{cE}} \qquad (4.27)$$

where R_{cE} is the room constant for the enclosure interior m² units.
In view of the simplifying assumption already made, there will be no great error if we replace R_{cE}, by A_E, the absorption inside the enclosure. (This has the added advantage of avoiding confusion between R_{cE} and R, the sound reduction index of the enclosure walls).
Substituting equation (4.26) and (4.27) into equation (4.25) gives the reduction in reverberant sound pressure level in a room, due to the enclosure of a source in the same room.

$$SPL_1 - SPL_2 = R - \log S_E + 10 \log A_E \qquad (4.28)$$

where SPL_1 and SPL_2 are respectively, the reverberant sound pressure levels in the room before and after enclosure of the source, dB

R is the sound reduction index of the enclosure wall

S_E is the amount of surface area of the enclosure radiating into the room, m²

A_E is the total absorption inside the enclosure, $S_E \bar{\alpha}_E$, m² units

$\bar{\alpha}_E$ is the average absorption coefficient inside the enclosure.

EXAMPLE 4.11

The reverberant sound pressure level in a room due to a water cooled refrigeration compressor in the same room, is to be reduced by providing an acoustic enclosure. The physical shape of the machine is effectively a rectangular cube 1 m × 2 m × 1 m high. The enclosure dimensions are 2 m × 3 m × 2 m high. The interior surfaces of the enclosure will be lined with 50 mm thick mineral wool blanket having the absorption characteristics shown in the table below. The floor and machine surfaces can be assumed to have the absorptive properties of concrete. Calculate the sound reduction index necessary for the enclosure walls and roof, if the reverberant sound pressure level in the room is not to exceed NC45.

Internal surface area of enclosure walls	= 26 m²
Surface area of machine	= 8 m²
Floor area (not covered by machine)	= 4 m²
Total internal surface area	= 38 m²

Octave Band Centre Freq.	Hz	63	125	250	500	1000	2000	4000	8000
(i) α concrete (Appendix A)			·01	·01	·01	·02	·02	·02	·03	·03
(ii) $S\alpha$ concrete (S = 12 m²) m²		·12	·12	·12	·24	·24	·24	·36	·36
(iii) α lining (Appendix A)			·10	·20	·45	·65	·75	·80	·80	·80
(iv) $S\alpha$ lining (S = 26 m²) m²		2·6	5·2	11·7	16·9	19·5	20·8	20·8	20·8
(v) A_E = (ii) + (iv) m²		2·72	5·32	11·82	17·14	19·74	21·04	21·16	21·16
(vi) 10 log A_E dB		4	7	11	12	13	13	13	13
(vii) 10 log S_E (S_E = 26 m²) dB		14	14	14	14	14	14	14	14
(viii) SPL_1 (measured) dB		70	78	80	82	80	82	80	75
(ix) SPL_2 (NC45, fig. 2.8) dB		67	60	54	49	46	44	43	41
(x) From eqn. (4.28) R = (viii) − (ix) + (vii) − (vi) dB		13	25	29	35	35	39	38	35

CHAPTER 5

Calculation of noise in ventilating systems

So far we have been concerned with noise which has travelled freely away from a source into a relatively large space—out of doors, into a room and between rooms. Ventilating systems pose a particular class of problem in engineering acoustics in that the noise energy produced by the primary source (usually the fan) is constrained to propagate along the ducting forming the air distribution system. This means of course that the inverse square law which governed the change of sound pressure level with distance from a source in free space, or in the direct radiation field in a room, no longer applies. In a duct system the only changes of sound pressure level are those due to loss of energy from such effects as wall absorption, reflection at bends and changes of section (all of which will be described later). In fact, if the duct was very long and straight, of constant cross sectional area, and had very heavy rigid walls, there would be very little change of sound pressure level along its entire length, and what change there was, would be largely due to the molecular absorption of air, as described in Chapter 4.

The reason for this was also explained in Chapter 4. If the source is allowed to radiate freely in all directions, the energy has to spread itself over a larger and larger area as distance from the source is increased. Because the area over which a given amount of power is distributed, increases as the square of the distance from the source, the acoustic intensity (energy flow rate/unit area) decreases as the distance squared. Since sound pressure level is virtually the same thing as intensity level we get the well known relationship of sound pressure level decreasing as 20 log r, (equation (4.4)).

If all the energy is constricted to pass along a duct of constant cross sectional area however, and there are no losses by absorption or reflection, then at any point along the duct there will always be the same amount of energy passing through that section. That is, the acoustic intensity is constant along the duct, and hence so is the sound pressure level.

Distance from the fan along a duct run, therefore, does not come into the calculation of noise in a ventilating system, *except* (and this is very important), insofar as it determines how much duct wall area is available to extract acoustic energy from the sound field by absorption, and how many energy reducing elements like bends and branches, there are between the observer and the fan.

The problem

Having established this fundamental point, we can now consider how sound energy is affected by travelling through a ventilating system from source to observer, and hence calculate the amount of noise likely to be produced by any given system. First, let us define our objective. Figure 5.1 shows schematically the basic elements of a ventilating system. It shows that we have three sets of calculations to perform in order to make a complete assessment of the system.

1. The fundamental and most important problem is the prediction of the sound pressure level that will result in the ventilated room due to the propagation of energy from the primary source—the fan. The sound energy produced by the fan is fed into the transmission path—that is, the system of ducting which distributes the air. The sound energy then leaves the ducting system, to be radiated from the grilles, diffusers, or other terminal devices, and reaches the occupants of the ventilated space.
2. We also have to predict the effect of sound energy being fed into the ducting system by sources other than the fan. These are represented on the overall energy flow diagram by a number of inputs labelled, collectively, secondary sources. There may be a variety of such sources in any given system, each of which contributes locally a certain amount of energy to add to the main flow. Typically, this would include noise generated by airflow through bends, dampers, heater batteries, and other elements which are likely to produce separated air flow conditions.
3. Finally we have to calculate what the effect will be of acoustic energy either leaving the system at points other than the duct termination, or by-passing the system altogether. Examples of this so-called flanking transmission include noise radiated by the fan casing, and noise transmitted through the duct walls. All such energy flows are indicated as dotted lines in figure 5.1.

Each of these calculations will now be explained in turn.

Transmission through the duct system

Dealing with the primary transmission first, the problem can conveniently be divided into three steps.

(a) Determine the total sound power fed into the system by the fan.
(b) Calculate by how much the fan sound energy will be attenuated by each of the various elements of the ducting forming the air distribution system.
(c) Calculate the amount of energy radiated from the duct termination to the nearest occupied position in the ventilated space.

G

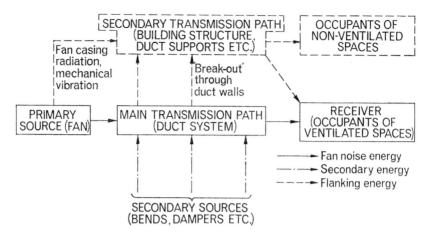

Fig. 5.1. Acoustic energy flow in a ventilating system

Sound power level of the fan

Without doubt the most reliable method of determining the amount of acoustic energy fed into the system is to get the fan manufacturer to provide sound power levels in each octave band of frequency, which have been determined by one or other of the standard test methods—for example British Standard 848 Part 2. Preferably the data should be given for a range of duties which includes the design duty, as shown in figure 5.2. This shows the effect on noise, of operating at off-design conditions, which enables one to make appropriate allowances when considering noise control measures.

Having said this, there will be instances of course when detailed information on the noise characteristics of the fan is not available. This often happens in the design stage of a system, when only the required duty has been established, but not the type or make of fan to produce it. Then one has to use one or other of the empirical formulae that are available to estimate the likely sound power level that will be produced. Three such formulae, originally developed by Beranek, which have been found to give reasonably accurate predictions are as follows:

$$SWL = 77 + 10 \log kW + 10 \log P \ dB$$
$$SWL = 25 + 10 \log Q + 20 \log P \ dB \qquad (5.1)$$
$$SWL = 130 + 20 \log kW - 10 \log Q \ dB$$

Where SWL = overall sound power level in the octave frequency bands from 31·5 Hz to 8000 Hz.

kW = Rated motor power, kW

P = Static pressure developed by the fan, mm w.g.

Q = Volume flow delivered, m³/h.

Any one of the above may be used, depending upon which details of the systems are known. To distribute the overall sound power level thus obtained into octave band sound power levels, the decibel correction shown in Table 5.1 should be applied.

TABLE 5.1

Corrections to obtain octave band spectra for various fan types

Octave Band Centre Frequency	*Hz*	63	125	250	500	1000	2000	4000	8000
					Add to overall sound power level dB				
Centrifugal:									
Backward curved blades		−4	−6	−9	−11	−13	−16	−19	−22
Forward curved blades		−2	−6	−13	−18	−19	−22	−25	−30
Radial blades		−3	−5	−11	−12	−15	−20	−23	−26
Axial		−7	−9	−7	−7	−8	−11	−16	−18
Mixed flow		0	−3	−6	−6	−10	−15	−21	−27

EXAMPLE 5.1

A ventilating system is designed to distribute 13000 m³/h of air, at which volume flow the resistance of the system is expected to amount to 17 mm static water gauge. In the absence of fan manufacturers data, estimate the likely sound power level to be fed into the system if an axial flow fan with aerofoil shaped blades is used.

From equation 5.1, SWL = 25 + 10 log (13000) + 20 log (17) dB

$$= 90 \text{ dB}$$

Octave Band Centre Freq	Hz	63	125	250	500	1000	2000	4000	8000
Overall SWL	dB	90	90	90	90	90	90	90	90
Spectrum correction (Table 5.1)	dB	−7	−9	−7	−7	−8	−11	−16	−18
Octave band SWL	dB	83	81	83	83	82	79	74	72

Attenuation in the duct system

Although in the introductory remarks reference was made to sound pressure level inside the duct, it is fortunately not necessary to calculate sound pressure level at every point along the system. We need to know only by how much the original energy is reduced as it passes down the system, so we can say how much of the original fan sound power is left to be radiated from the end. All we require is the attenuation of the input sound power level in decibels, by each element of the duct system. In the discussions which follow, it is assumed that there is no acoustic treatment in the system other perhaps than that included in the design of proprietary elements which may be present. The analysis of acoustic treatment in duct systems is discussed in detail in Chapter 6 and 7.

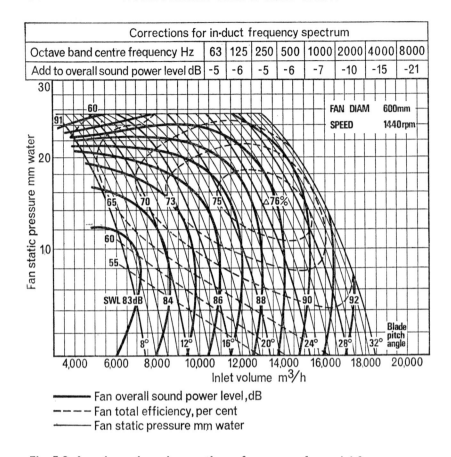

Corrections for in-duct frequency spectrum								
Octave band centre frequency Hz	63	125	250	500	1000	2000	4000	8000
Add to overall sound power level dB	-5	-6	-5	-6	-7	-10	-15	-21

————— Fan overall sound power level, dB
– – – – Fan total efficiency, per cent
——·— Fan static pressure mm water

Fig. 5.2. Aerodynamic and acoustic performance of an axial fan

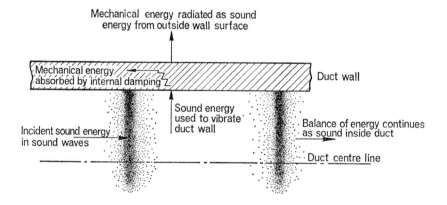

Fig. 5.3. Energy balance on element of duct wall

(a) *Plain duct runs*

It may at first seem surprising that sound can be attenuated when passing along a channel of constant area with steel walls. In fact, we said in the introduction to this section that if the walls are perfectly rigid there is no loss of energy except perhaps that due to molecular absorption of air over long distances.

The reason that in practice we do get attenuation is of course that real duct walls are not rigid. The action of the fluctuating acoustic pressures inside the duct is to vibrate the duct walls. Of that energy, some will be re-radiated as airborne noise on the outside of the duct, and this may cause problems in rooms through which the ducting runs, as we shall see later. The rest of it will be transformed into heat energy in overcoming the internal damping of the material from which the duct is constructed. The energy flow here is summarised in the sketch in figure 5.3.

Wherever the energy goes however, the net result is that the original energy, i.e. the sound power level inside the duct, has been reduced. Since the process is continuous along the length of the duct, it is convenient to express the rate of energy loss in decibels reduction of sound power per metre run of ducting. Typical values of attenuation in each frequency band, for different sizes of both circular and rectangular sheet metal ducts, are shown in figure 5.4.

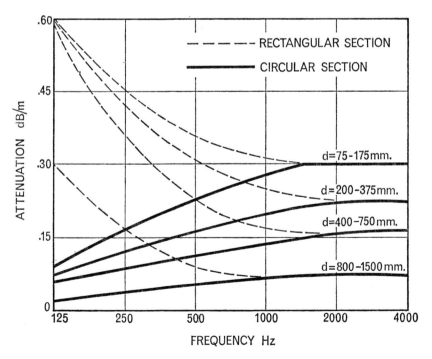

Fig. 5.4. Approximate attenuation in plain ducts of minimum width d

It is interesting to note that at low frequencies, rectangular ducting gives much higher attenuation than circular ducting. This is because the walls of rectangular ducts are relatively much less stiff than the wall of a circular duct of equivalent size. As explained in Chapter 6 the transmission of low frequency noise through a partition varies inversely as its stiffness, hence more energy is extracted from inside rectangular ducts than from circular ones. At higher frequencies, again as explained in Chapter 6, the transmission is governed by the superficial mass of the partition which, for ducts of similar material will be the same for both rectangular and circular walls—hence the equality of attenuation.

(b) *Bends*

The attenuation of sound energy at bends is by a process of reflection back towards the source, rather by the absorption mechanism of plain duct runs. As might be expected this attenuation is greater for 90° elbows

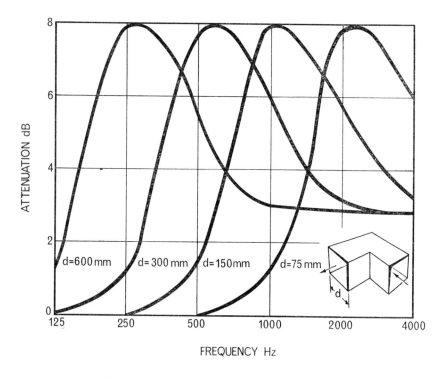

FREQUENCY Hz

Fig. 5.5. Approximate attenuation of unlined 90° elbows of width d

where the reflecting surface is normal to the propagation path of the incident wave. There is also a "resonance" effect which gives peak attenuation at the frequency whose wavelength is exactly one half of the duct width. Figure 5.5 shows the attenuation to be expected at plain (unlined) 90° bends of various widths, and demonstrates clearly this effect. Long radius bends, or even mitre bends with long turning vanes, generally give much less reduction, and to be conservative are usually ignored. As a general guide, the lower the aerodynamic resistance of the bend, the lower will be the attenuation of sound energy it affords.

(c) *Branches*

Strictly speaking there is no nett loss of energy at a branch. Rather, it simply divides between the main and take-off ducts in the same way as the airflow does. There is no reflection or absorption mechanism by which

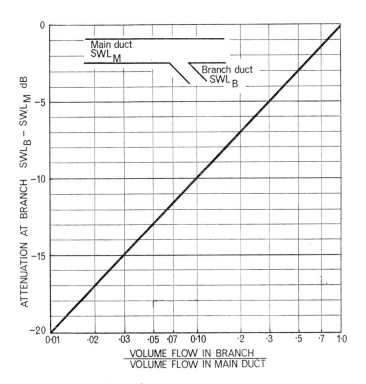

Fig. 5.6. Attenuation at branches

the total energy after the branch is less than the total approaching the branch. On the other hand, if we consider the duct termination at the end of one branch, there is obviously less energy arriving there than was originally present before the branch. Thus the branch must be regarded as having attenuated some of the original energy, by re-directing it elsewhere (i.e. along the rest of the main ducting). For engineering purposes, it is sufficiently accurate to assume that the division of sound energy at a branch is in the same proportion as the division of air flow. The attenuation in any one branch is then given by:

$$\text{Attenuation} = 10 \log\left\{\frac{\text{volume flow of air in branch considered}}{\text{total volume flow of air up to branch}}\right\} \text{dB} \quad (5.2)$$

This is shown graphically for various percentage divisions of airflow in figure 5.6.

(d) *Duct terminations*

After various degrees of attenuation, by the duct runs, at bends, and at branches, what is left of the original input energy arrives at the end of the duct where it opens into the volume of the ventilated room. However, not all of this energy actually radiates into the room. By the principle of reflection, some of it passes back along the duct and therefore, as far as the room is concerned, attenuated. The mathematical explanation for this is rather involved, but it can be explained qualitatively if we recall our original concept of the structure of sound waves. We have explained the propagation of acoustic energy along the duct in terms of travelling waves of pressure. Now, if we consider just a small elemental length of the duct, the "slug" of air in that element physically moves over a short distance as the pressure wave approaches. (Just as the air immediately next to the piston did, in our first model—see figure 1.1.) As long as the immediately adjacent element of air is the same size (and therefore mass), we say that the "acoustic impedance", or resistance to propagation of the wave, is constant.

There is then no change of energy along the propagation path (along the duct)—apart of course from the progressive absorption of energy by the duct walls, as described previously. The element of air just at the duct opening, however, finds itself suddenly having to move against a much larger mass of air contained in the region of the room space around the end of the duct. This change of mass constitutes a change of acoustic impedance, and, just as we saw in Chapter 4, when a sound wave travelling in a medium with a certain impedance suddenly meets a medium with a different impedance, some of its energy passes on into the new medium (the volume of the room) and some is reflected back into the old medium (the duct space).

Now the amount of energy reflected in this way is frequency dependent. More precisely, in the case of a duct termination, the amount of energy reflected depends on the ratio of the wavelength of the sound to the size of the duct. At low frequencies, where wavelengths are generally much larger than the duct size, the situation is as described above. That is to say, the elements of air in the duct tend to move as "blocks" which are of the same cross section as the duct. High frequency sound on the other hand tends to be "beamed" down the centre of the duct—the centre of the "block" of air moving with greater amplitude than the region nearest the walls. The centre region of the "block", the one carrying nearly all the energy of the waves at that frequency, acts in fact as though the duct walls were not present. Consequently, when the high frequency wave emerges from the duct, it encounters no change of conditions—most of its energy is still being transmitted via the relatively small regions of air in line with the duct axis. There is then little or no reflection of the wave back along the duct.

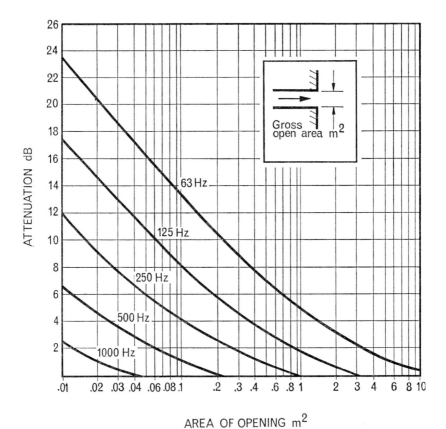

Fig. 5.7. Attenuation at duct outlets

Figure 5.7 summarises the attenuation of energy to be expected by reflection from a duct opening. Note here that the open area referred to is the gross open area of the terminal grille or diffuser, neglecting vanes, louvres etc., which normally do not have a marked effect on reflection except perhaps at very high frequencies (wavelengths comparable with the vane size).

All the foregoing remarks apply to duct terminations which are fitted with what might be termed "conventional" grilles or diffusers. In some cases however, the terminal unit itself may be a noise attenuating unit. The most usual example nowadays is the high velocity system induction unit. Most manufacturers will be able to supply insertion loss figures for such units, which should be used in place of the reflection loss figures described above.

(e) *Plenum chambers*

Where plenum chambers form part of the system through which the fan noise has to propagate, they can provide attenuation. A general layout is shown in figure 5.8 and the effect upon sound energy arriving at the inlet is rather like entering a small room and then passing from the room into a duct on the other side (see "Cross-talk"). As in a room, the sound pressure level at the outlet point (and hence the sound power leaving), will comprise the energy radiated directly to that point from the inlet, and the reverberant energy in the chamber. The approximate loss in sound power across the plenum is given by

$$\text{SWL}_1 - \text{SWL}_2 = 10 \log S_2 \left\{ \frac{\cos \theta}{2\pi d^2} + \frac{1}{R_c} \right\} \text{dB} \qquad (5.3)$$

where S_2 is the outlet area, m^2

   d is the slant distance from centre of inlet to centre of outlet, m

   θ is the angle d makes with the inlet axis

   R_c is the "room constant" of the plenum m^2 units $= \dfrac{S_T \bar{\alpha}}{1 - \bar{\alpha}}$

   S_T is the total internal surface area of the plenum (including inlet and outlet areas), m^2

   $\bar{\alpha}$ is the average absorption co-efficient of the internal surfaces of the plenum (equation 4.12)

   Note when calculating $\bar{\alpha}$ that inlet and outlet areas are assumed to have an absorption co-efficient of 1.0.

The nett attenuation across a plenum chamber will in fact be higher than that predicted by equation (5.3), because no account is taken there of losses due to reflection at the inlet. For the complete attenuation therefore, the loss due to reflection given in figure 5.7 should be added to the theoretical values calculated from equation (5.3).

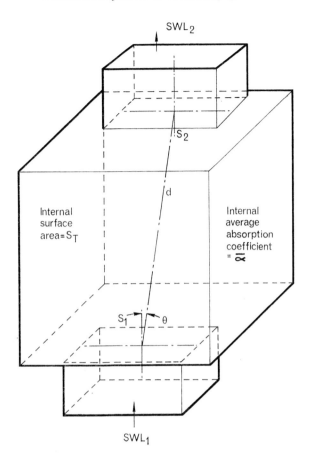

Fig. 5.8. Geometry of plenum chamber

The method of calculation

We now have sufficient information to be able to predict the room sound pressure level that will result from the transmission of fan noise through the system.

The calculation can be summarised as follows.

(a) *Fan to duct termination*

    (i) Write down the sound power level in each octave band of frequency which will be fed into the system by the fan. This information will be obtained either directly from the fan manufacturer, or as a pre-liminary estimate from equation (5.1).

(ii) For each octave band in turn, reduce the input sound power level by the attenuation afforded by the various elements of the system.
   i.e. For plain duct runs,   use fig. 5.4.
        For bends,   use fig. 5.5.
        For branches,   use fig. 5.6, or equation (5.2).
        For duct termination,   use fig. 5.7, or manufacturers insertion loss figures.
   For a plenum chamber, use equation (5.3) plus fig. 5.7.

Note:
There may be other elements in the system like proprietary mixing boxes or certain types of filters, which may have sound attenuating characteristics (not to be confused with sound generating characteristics which are discussed later under "Secondary noise generation"). If so, their acoustic insertion loss in decibels, for the particular conditions of operation, should be obtained from the manufacturer, and added to the attenuation from the other duct elements described.

The result will then be the amount of sound energy (expressed as sound power level), which is available at the grille or diffuser to radiate into the occupied space.

EXAMPLE 5.2

The simple system shown in the sketch below is located in the roof space of a storage area between two offices. The sound power level produced by the fan is known from manufacturer's data. Estimate the sound power level of the noise which will be introduced into Office A by one outlet.

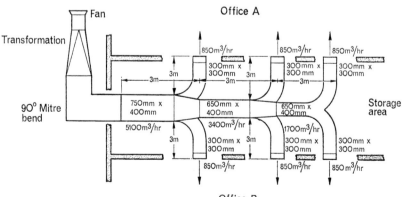

Where a number of outlets from a system feed into the same room it is normal to consider only the outlet nearest the fan—the others being assumed to radiate the same amount of sound power. This does, of course, over estimate the total sound power radiated into the room, but it does have the merit of erring on the "safe" side. The analysis up to the first grille is carried out as follows:

Octave Band Centre Freq.	Hz	63	125	250	500	1000	2000	4000	8000
(i) Fan SWL (Manufacturers data)	dB	74	73	74	73	72	69	64	58
(ii) 400 mm (min) rect. duct 3 m long (fig. 5.4)	dB	−3	−2	−1	−1	0	0	0	0
(iii) 300 mm rect. duct 3 m long (fig. 5.4)	dB	−3	−2	−1	−1	−1	−1	−1	−1
(iv) 750 mm wide 90° elbow (fig. 5.5)	dB	0	−2	−8	−5	−3	−3	−3	−3
(v) Radiussed bend at branch	dB	0	0	0	0	0	0	0	0
(vi) Sound power loss at branch (ratio = ·167) fig. 5.6	dB	−8	−8	−8	−8	−8	−8	−8	−8
(vii) Reflection loss at outlet (fig. 5.7—area = ·09 m²)	dB	−14	−8	−4	−1	0	0	0	0
SWL radiated into room	dB	46	51	52	57	60	57	52	46

It is clear from inspection of the layout that the sound power radiated from the centre grille would be lower than this by the amount of attenuation afforded by an extra 3 m length of 400 mm ducting (second line of table). Also the sound power radiated by the end grille would be lower again by the attenuation afforded by an additional 3 m length of 300 mm ducting (third line of table). As stated above however, it is customary to make the estimate conservative by assuming the sound power radiated from the first grille is representative of all the grilles on the system which enter the room.

(b) *Duct termination to room*

We saw in Chapter 4 that the relationship between the sound power level SWL of a source in an enclosed space whose acoustic properties were described by the room constant R_c, and the sound pressure level SPL at a point distance r and angle θ from the source, was given by (equation (4.17)).

$$SPL = SWL + 10 \log \left[\frac{Q_\theta}{4\pi r^2} + \frac{4}{R_c} \right] dB$$

When evaluating this expression it is convenient to calculate the direct and reverberant sound pressure levels separately, and add the two logarithmically using, for example, table 1.2.

The following procedure will result in the room sound pressure level due to one grille only. When there is more than one in the same room, the calculation should be repeated for each. Normally, additional grilles will affect only the reverberant level in the room, the direct level at any point being determined mainly by the nearest grille.

(i) *Direct sound pressure level*

The direct sound pressure level is obtained from the first term in the bracket, i.e.

$$SPL_D = SWL - 20 \log r + DI(\theta) - 11 \text{ dB} \qquad (5.4)$$

where SWL is the sound power level at the duct termination (evaluated from (a) above)

   r is the distance of the observation point in the room from the centre of the duct termination, m.

   $DI(\theta)$ is the directivity index for angle θ between r and the duct axis $(= 10 \log Q_\theta)$ dB

   Q_θ is the directivity factor at angle θ.

The directivity factor Q_θ is important when considering radiation from grilles and diffusers, for two reasons.

First, the directional pattern of radiation depends upon the position of the unit in relation to walls, ceilings and similar reflecting surfaces. If the grille were a source of the same power level hung in free space near the centre of the room, it would be free to radiate in all directions (see fig. 5.9 (a)). If, as is more usual, it is mounted flush with a wall or the ceiling somewhere near the centre of that surface, all the energy it radiates is constrained to propagate forward into a hemispherical region in the room. Then an observer in the same position relative to the grille would receive twice the amount of energy he would have received in the "free-space" condition (see fig. 5.9 (b)).

If the grille is mounted in the junction of one wall and the ceiling its sound energy is constrained to radiate in a quarter sphere, resulting in the observer receiving four times the energy (fig. 5.9 (c)). If it is mounted in the corner formed by two walls and the ceiling, the energy flow is constrained to one eighth of a sphere, resulting in an eightfold increase of energy at the observer.

Second, the directional pattern of the radiation depends upon the frequency, or rather, upon the wavelength considered, compared with the size of the grille. When this ratio is large, i.e. for low frequency noise and small grilles, the energy tends to be radiated equally in all directions (subject of course to its position relative to reflecting surfaces as explained above), so that, at a given distance from the grille, the sound pressure level will be independent of angular direction from the grille axis. At high frequencies however, the energy tends to be "beamed" along the axis, of the grille, as indicated in fig. 5.10.

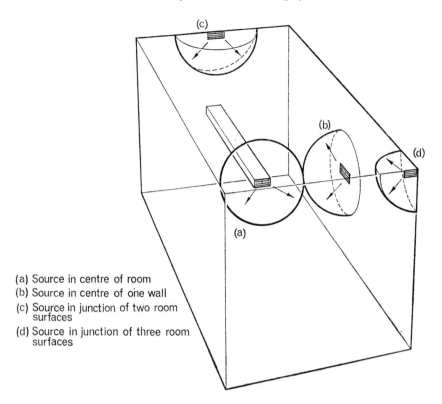

(a) Source in centre of room
(b) Source in centre of one wall
(c) Source in junction of two room surfaces
(d) Source in junction of three room surfaces

Fig. 5.9. Radiation patterns for a non-directional source in various room locations

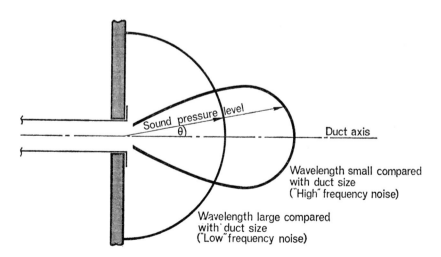

Fig. 5.10. Effect of frequency on radiation pattern

This means that the sound pressure levels of the higher frequency octave bands are generally higher directly in line with the grille axis, than they are at positions to the side. For this reason it is always the practice when calculating the noise from ventilating systems, to consider as the worst case, the observer directly in line with the duct termination, and the directivity factor Q is evaluated at 0°. Values of DI(θ) (= 10 log Q_θ) which combine both wavelength and grille position effects, are shown in fig. 5.11.

(ii) *Reverberant sound pressure level*

The reverberant sound level is obtained from the second term in the bracket in equation (4.17), i.e.

$$SPL_R = SWL - 10 \log R_c + 6 \text{ dB} \tag{5.5}$$

where SWL is the sound power level at the duct termination (evaluated from (a))

R_e is the room constant, $= S \dfrac{\bar{\alpha}}{1-\bar{\alpha}}$, m² units

S is the total surface area of the room, m²

$\bar{\alpha}$ is the average absorption coefficient in the room (equation (4.12)).

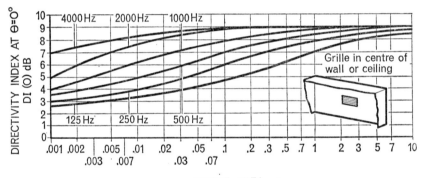

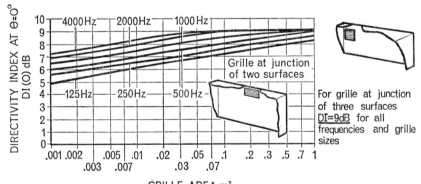

Fig. 5.11. Values of directivity index on grille axis

To summarise, for the room sound pressure level due to fan noise emanating from a particular grille.

(1) Calculate the sound power level at the duct termination following the procedure described previously.
(2) Calculate the direct sound pressure level at the observation point in the room using equation (5.4) and Fig. 5.11.
(3) Calculate the reverberant sound pressure level in the room using equation (5.5).
(4) Add the direct and reverberant sound pressure levels to give the total sound pressure level at the observation point, using Table 1.2.

EXAMPLE 5.3

For the system described in example 5.2, calculate the sound pressure level in office A, at the nearest occupied position to a supply grille, which is given to be 1·1 m from the grille and directly in line with its axis. The office may be assumed to be the same size and layout as the one described in example 4.6 with values of room constant R_c evaluated in example 4.7 (line (iii)), and the grilles are located in the wall, near the junction with the ceiling.

Octave Band Centre Freq	Hz	63	125	250	500	1000	2000	4000	8000
A. DIRECT SPL (eqn. 5.4))									
Input SWL (example 5.2)	dB	46	51	52	57	60	57	52	46
− (20 log r + 11)(r = 1·1 m)	dB	−12	−12	−12	−12	−12	−12	−12	−12
DI (θ) (fig. 5.11—area = ·09 m²)	dB	+6	+7	+8	+8	+9	+9	+9	+9
DIRECT SPL	dB	40	46	48	53	57	54	49	43
B. REVERBERANT SPL (eqn. (5.5))									
Input SWL (example 5.2) + 6	dB	52	57	58	63	66	63	58	52
−10 log R_c (example 4.7, line (iii))	dB	−16	−17	−21	−24	−25	−26	−26	−26
Contribution from 3 grilles (+ 10 log (3))	dB	+5	+5	+5	+5	+5	+5	+5	+5
REVERBERANT SPL	dB	41	45	42	44	46	42	37	31
Direct + Rev. SPL's (Table 1.2)	dB	44	49	49	54	57	54	49	43

Note that the direct sound pressure level is usually determined only by the grille nearest to the observation point. On the other hand, all the grilles feeding sound energy into the room contribute to the reverberant level. Therefore the reverberant sound pressure level due to a single grille must be increased by the factor 10 log (number of grilles contributing). Again this assumes that all the grilles are contributing equal amounts of sound power.

Calculation of atmospheric side sound levels

One point that is often overlooked when assessing a ventilating system for noise, is that sound travels equally well in both directions from the fan. Centrifugal, axial, or mixed flow, all produce approximately the same sound power on the inlet side as on the discharge side. The air velocities in the ducting of even high velocity systems—say up to 20 m/sec are so small compared to the velocity of acoustic waves in the duct, 345 m/sec, that the efficiency of sound propagation is just about the same upstream as it is downstream. This means that for a complete acoustic assessment of a ventilating or air conditioning system, we have to calculate how much sound emerges on the atmospheric side of the fan as well as on the system side, irrespective of whether we have a supply or extract system.

(a) *Open running fan*

If the fan is running open, inside an enclosed space like a plant room or a plant area above a false ceiling we may want to calculate the reverberant level in the plant space in order to determine whether there will be a problem from airborne noise transmitted through the partition into adjacent rooms. The calculation is exactly the same as the room calculation described in Chapter 4. Sound pressure level in the plant room can be calculated from equation (4.17), using the fan sound power level (manufacturers' data or equation (5.1)), as the sound power level of the source.

(b) *Atmospheric ducting*

If the fan is drawing or discharging through an atmospheric louvre fixed in the plant room wall there may be a problem with fan noise radiated to adjacent property—residential areas, hospital wards, schools, or office premises for example. The first step is to calculate the sound power level inside the atmospheric ducting at the louvre. The procedure here is exactly the same as that described previously in the section "transmission through the duct system".

Calculation of the amount of noise radiated from the atmospheric louvre, is also much the same as the procedure described previously for calculating the radiation from a room grille or diffuser. Here however, we are concerned only with the direct sound pressure level.

As before, the sound pressure level at distance r from the centre of the louvre, and angle θ to the axis is given by equation (5.4) i.e.

$$\text{SPL} = \text{SWL} - 20 \log r + \text{DI}(\theta) - 11 \text{ dB}$$

where the quantities are as defined in equation (5.4).

For angles directly in line with the axis of the louvre ($\theta = 0°$), the values of directivity index shown in fig. 5.11 (grille in centre of wall) will again apply. With atmospheric louvres however, we have to be more general—being usually concerned with sound pressure level at some nearby fixed point, which may be in any angular direction relative to the axis. In that case we have to know the directivity index at all angles, and this is given in fig. 5.12.

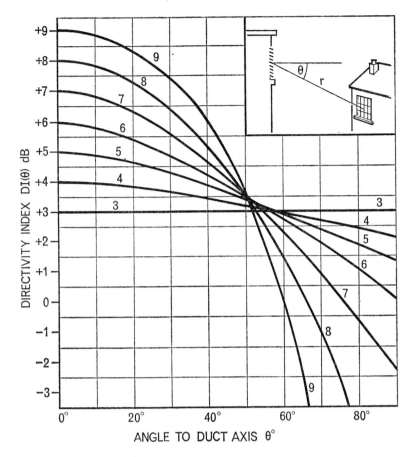

Fig. 5.12. Directivity index for radiation from atmospheric louvres

The numbers on the curves here refer to the directivity index at 0°. To determine the directivity index at another angle, first find the directivity at 0° from fig. 5.11, then move along the appropriate curve on fig. 5.12, until the vertical line passing through the angle of interest (horizontal scale) is intersected. The directivity index at that angle is then read off the vertical scale, at the point horizontally opposite the intersection.

It is interesting to note that curve 3 shows a directivity index of +3 dB irrespective of angle from the louvre axis. Referring back to fig. 5.11, we see that this curve generally applies for frequencies whose wavelengths are large compared to the louvre dimensions. This is because under those conditions the radiation from the louvre tends to be unidirectional, and so we have the simple model of a unidirectional source radiating into a hemispherical space. As we saw in equations (4.5), and (4.7), the directivity index is then 3 dB.

EXAMPLE 5.4

It is decided to reduce plant-room noise levels due to the inlet of the fan shown in example 5.2, by ducting the inlet via a transformation piece, to a fresh air inlet louvre, 1 m square, located in an outside wall. If the area of this wall is large compared with that of the louvre, calculate the sound pressure level which will be produced outside an apartment window which is 20 m away from the louvre in a direction 35° to the louvre axis.

We assume that the only loss of energy in travelling from fan inlet to outside the louvre is by reflection at the louvre opening itself.

Octave Band Centre Freq	Hz	63	125	250	500	1000	2000	4000	8000
(i) Fan SWL (example 5.2)	dB	74	73	74	73	72	69	64	58
(ii) Reflection at louvre (fig. 5.7) (1 m²)	dB	−5	−2	0	0	0	0	0	0
(iii) SWL radiated from louvre	dB	69	71	74	73	72	69	64	58
(iv) DI(0°) (fig. 5.11) (area = 1 m²)	dB	+7	+7	+8	+9	+9	+9	+9	+9
(v) DI(35°) (fig. 5.12)	dB	+5	+5	+6	+7	+7	+7	+7	+7
(vi) − (20 log r + 11) (r = 20 m)	dB	−37	−37	−37	−37	−37	−37	−37	−37
SPL at 20 m, 35° = (iii)+(v)+(vi)	dB	37	39	43	43	42	39	34	28

Secondary sources

When discussing the overall problem of the acoustic assessment of a ventilating system, we saw in fig. 5.1 that the second important task was to calculate how much acoustic energy would be fed into the system by sources other than the fan. Unfortunately this includes potentially every solid body in the system which is exposed to moving air. Airflow over any rigid surface generates a turbulent flow to some degree or other. The action of the turbulent flow on a solid surface is to set up areas of rapidly fluctuating pressure on the surface. In our first examination of the mechanism by which sound could be generated, in Chapter 1, we used the model of a moving surface—the face of a piston. In fact we could have generated sound without moving the piston, had we been able somehow to arrange for a fluctuating pressure to be set up in the elemental layer of air just next to the piston face. As a matter of interest the efficiency of generating acoustic energy in this way would have been less than by moving the piston. This is relative though—we could still have generated enough noise to be objectionable had the pressure fluctuation been strong enough. In ventilating systems they frequently are—particularly in high velocity systems. We shall now examine how much noise can be generated.

It is convenient to consider the various noise generating elements under two headings.

(i) Elements feeding secondary noise energy into the duct
  duct runs
  bends
  branches
  contractions
  dampers
  proprietary fittings (heater coils, mixing boxes, etc.).
(ii) Terminal units radiating secondary noise energy directly into the room
  grilles (with or without integral dampers)
  diffusers
  induction units
  proprietary terminal units.

(a) *In-duct elements*

For in-duct elements there is unfortunately very little data available from which we can make an accurate prediction of the amount of noise energy which will be added to the fan noise at that point in the system. As a guide to the orders of magnitude to be expected however, one may use the data given in Table 5.2.

TABLE 5.2
Air flow generated noise in duct fittings (after Stewart)

Fitting	*Overall sound power level dB (octave bands 250–8000 Hz)* K
Straight Duct	38
3:1 contraction (to 12 in. × 12 in.)	47
90° bends	
radiused	48 (est)
mitred with turning vanes	56
mitred without turning vanes	57
Duct with 90° tee (5 per cent draw-off)	55
Damper: Open	44
15° closed	53
45° closed	65

Corrections to give octave band SWL

Octave Band Centre Freq.	Hz	250	500	1000	2000	4000	8000
Spectrum correction to overall SWL	dB	−7	−7	−8	−10	−17	−29

These figures are for the specific case of ducting 300 mm × 300 mm with a flow of 10 m/sec. To obtain sound power level for other sizes and velocities use the following extrapolation.

$$\text{SWL} = K + 10 \log S + 55 \log V - 45 \text{ dB} \qquad (5.6)$$

where SWL is the sound power level generated by the actual fitting, dB
  K is the datum power level of the fitting given in Table 5.2, dB
  S is the actual duct area, m²
  V is the actual velocity, m/sec.

It must be noted that these approximate predictions will only apply when the flow into the fitting is reasonably smooth. That is, they are predictions of the "self noise" generated by the fitting itself. When the oncoming flow is rough or non uniform—say, in the case of a damper immediately downstream of a bend—add at least 5 dB to the predicted sound power level.

Where the in-duct fittings are proprietary units, obtain from the manufacturer in-duct sound power levels generated in each octave bend from 63 Hz to 8000 Hz. Care must again be taken in interpreting such data. Often such tests will have been carried out following a standard test method, for which generally the approach velocity will be smooth. If the figures have not been obtained under flow conditions similar to those that will apply in the installation, an additional 5dB should be allowed for.

By one or other means then, we will have determined the additional sound power level which will be fed into the duct at the point where the noise generating element is located. All we need to do then, is to compare this with the sound power level at that point due to the fan. It can be seen from the worked example of the analysis of fan noise (example 5.2) that it is quite easy to establish what the sound power level due to the fan will be at any point along the system. If the secondary sound power level is 10 dB or more below the fan noise sound power level, we can ignore the secondary noise at that point in the system. If the difference is less than 10 dB, or if the secondary sound power level is greater than the sound power level of the fan noise, then the originally calculated fan noise at that point must be corrected using table 1.2. The originally calculated sound pressure level in the room will then be increased by the same amount. Needless to say, the procedure must be repeated for all secondary noise generating elements in the system.

EXAMPLE 5.5

The system described in example 5.2 incorporates a damper in each branch duct. When the system is operating it is anticipated that the damper will be about 30° closed. Under these conditions the maximum velocity through the damper is expected to be 8 m/sec. Estimate the effect on the total sound power radiated from a grille.

By interpolation in Table 5.2 we find that for a damper 30° closed, K is approximately 60 dB.

From equation (5.6), $SWL = 60 + 10 \log (0 \cdot 1) + 55 \log (8) - 45$ dB

$$= 55 \text{ dB}$$

The sound power level of the fan just before the grille (after this point the fan and damper noise will be affected together) can be obtained from the tabulated solution to example 5.2, by adding the attenuation for the various duct elements, excluding "reflection loss at outlet", i.e.

Octave Band Centre Frequency	Hz	250	500	1000	2000	4000	8000
SWL of fan noise before grille (ex. 5.2)	dB	56	58	60	57	52	46
SWL of damper noise (table 5.2)	dB	48	48	47	45	38	26
Total SWL before grille	dB	57	58	60	57	52	46

In this case the noise generated by the damper increased the total noise by only 1 dB at 250 Hz—not a significant amount. Had the branch take-off been of a form which generated strong turbulent flow on to the damper however, the damper sound power level would have increased by about 5 dB, which, bearing in mind the order of accuracy that can be expected from the estimate, would warrant a closer examination.

As a general guide, to avoid needless work, it is usually safe to ignore secondary noise in conventional systems, where main duct velocities do not exceed 7·5 m/sec and branch velocities do not exceed 3 m/sec, and where the noise requirements in the room are not particularly stringent—down to say NC40. For higher duct velocities, or for lower criteria it is as well to check on noise-producing elements at the room end of the system, unless it is immediately obvious from Table 5.2 that the sound power likely to be generated is much less than the fan sound power appearing at the grille.

(b) *Terminal units*

Since terminal units are usually of proprietary manufacture, it is nearly always possible to obtain data on their sound generation from the manufacturers. This is always to be preferred, but where the information is not available, one can make preliminary estimates as with in-duct elements.

For grilles a rough approximation to the overall sound power generated in the important speech interference octave bands can be obtained from

$$SWL = 55 \log V + 10 \log S + 5 \text{ dB} \qquad (5.7)$$

where SWL is the average sound power level generated in the octave bands
between 500 Hz and 4000 Hz, dB
V is the core velocity at the grille, m/sec.
S is the core area of the grille, m².

This equation applies to grilles with vertical or horizontal deflecting bars. Grilles consisting of plain perforated sheet will on average produce a sound power level about 10 dB less than predicted by equation (5.7). The distribution of the sound power into the octave bands can be assumed to be approximately the same as shown in Table 5.2.

It is very important to note that this simple prediction applies only to simple grilles. Where a damper unit is an integral part of the grille, quite large increases in sound power generated can occur due to the wakes from the damper blades impinging upon the grille blades as indicated in fig. 5.13. The impingement of turbulence in this manner sets up fluctuating pressures on the grille blades, additional to those generated by the grille blades themselves, hence more noise is generated.

Even if the damper is fully open an allowance of 5 dB over and above equation (5.7) should be made for its presence. The increase of noise beyond this when the damper is operated is difficult to predict, but one manufacturer quotes an increase of 8 dB for each doubling of pressure ratio across the unit. The same correction should be assumed, if the damper is a separate unit, but located nearer than one duct width to the grille.

Diffusers produce rather higher noise levels than grilles. An approximate formulae for the overall sound power level generated (125 Hz to 8000 Hz) by diffusers incorporating dampers, is given by:

$$\text{SWL} = 60 \log \text{V} + 13 \log \text{S} + 33 \text{ dB} \qquad (5.8)$$

where V is the *maximum* velocity at the damper, m/sec

S is the *minimum* open area at the particular damper setting, m².

Again, the corrections to convert the overall sound power level to octave band sound power levels can be assumed to be the same as those shown in Table 5.2.

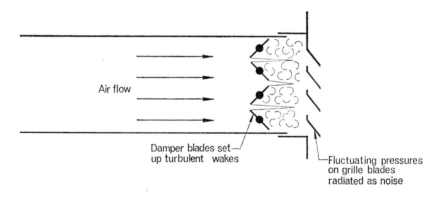

Air flow

Damper blades set up turbulent wakes

Fluctuating pressures on grille blades radiated as noise

Fig. 5.13. Mechanism of noise generation by dampers and grilles

For induction units there is virtually no data from which one can make a general prediction. One has to rely entirely upon manufacturer's data. Note however that room sound pressure levels below NC30 are extremely unlikely to be achieved with induction units in the room.

When one has sound power data for a particular terminal unit in the room, one compares this with the fan sound power which is available to be radiated from that terminal, as previously calculated following the method described earlier ("Transmission through the duct system"). Again, if the terminal sound power level is more than 10 dB below the sound power level of the fan at that point in the system, the room sound pressure level will be determined entirely by the fan noise. Otherwise, the nett sound power level at the duct termination will be the combination of terminal unit and fan sound power levels (Table 1.2). The previously calculated room sound pressure level must then be increased accordingly.

Indirect and flanking transmission

The final task in the overall assessment of the system is to predict the effect of acoustic energy leaving or bypassing the system, and appearing as airborne noise in either the ventilated room or in other rooms. Some of the more important paths for indirect transmission are shown in fig. 5.14.

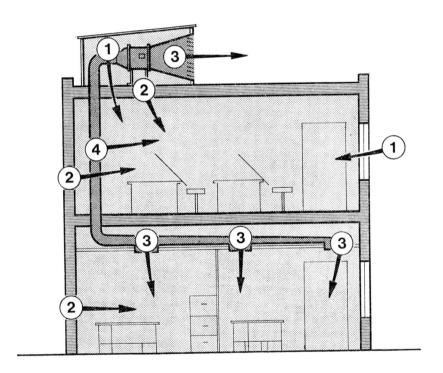

1. AIRBORNE NOISE FROM PLANT ROOM
2. STRUCTUREBORNE NOISE
3. DUCTBORNE NOISE
4. BREAK-OUT OF DUCTBORNE NOISE

Fig. 5.14. Noise transmission paths in a ventilating system

They can be summarised as follows:

  (i) Airborne noise from the plant room transmitted through the plant room walls and floor to adjacent rooms or to outside
  (ii) Duct-borne fan noise transmitted through the duct wall into rooms through which the ducting passes
  (iii) Mechanical vibration energy from the fan fed into the building structure and re-radiated into rooms as airborne noise.

Noise in the plant room

The noise level in a plant room due to a fan is usually the result of either noise inside the fan itself and associated ducting being transmitted through the fan casing and duct walls, or direct radiation of mechanical vibration from the fan casing and drive motor if this is external to the fan. (The case of an open running fan in a plant room we have already discussed under "calculation of atmospheric side sound levels".)

The first source is fairly amenable to calculation, and is discussed in more detail in the section below on duct "break-out". Briefly, we calculate the amount of sound *power* that emerges from inside the fan casing or plant room ducting, and then call this the sound power level of an equivalent source placed in the room. From there we calculate the room sound pressure level using equation (4.17), and eventually the sound pressure levels in areas adjacent to the plant room using the appropriate equation from (4.18) onwards.

The second source, radiation from the fan casing and drive motor, is unfortunately almost impossible to predict. The problem here is that the noise generating mechanisms are a function of the mechanical design of the particular unit, rather than being related to overall performance, as aerodynamic noise could be related to volume flow, overall static pressure developed, or shaft power, as in equation (5.1).

Noise appearing at the shaft rotational frequency for example will depend on the residual out-of-balance force that the manufacturer tolerates on the impeller, and on the mounting design. The radiation of noise from the drive motor depends upon its frame design, and, in the case of an axial fan, upon the efficiency of transmission of mechanical energy to the fan case.

The best one can do to predict plant room noise level, in the absence of figures from the manufacturer, is to extrapolate from measurements of reverberant sound pressure level in a room containing an identical unit. If the reverberant sound pressure level in a test room with room constant R_{cT}, is SPL_T, then the sound power level of the unit is from equation (4.17)

$$SWL_T = SPL_T - 10 \log \left(\frac{4}{R_{cT}} \right) \text{ dB} \qquad (5.9)$$

If the room constant for the design plant room is then R_{cP}, again from equation (4.17), the reverberant sound pressure level in the plant room will be

$$SPL_P = SWL_T + 10 \log \left(\frac{4}{R_{cP}} \right) \text{ dB}$$

or, using equation (5.9)

$$SPL_P = SPL_T + 10 \log \left(\frac{R_{cT}}{R_{cP}} \right) \text{ dB} \qquad (5.10)$$

If this method of predicting fan casing noise is to be used, care must be taken to ensure that with the test arrangement, only the reverberant sound pressure level, SPL_T, due to the fan casing noise is measured. That is to say both inlet to, and outlet from the fan are ducted away, and if necessary the ducting is lagged (see Chapter 7). Both fan performance during test, and the mounting arrangement, should be as close to the actual conditions as possible.

Noise "break-out" from ducts

When we were discussing the transmission of sound energy through the duct system we saw that the energy was decreased during its passage along a duct by absorption at the walls. As figure 5.3 showed, some of this energy was transformed into heat by the internal damping of the duct walls, and the rest was radiated as airborne noise from the outside of the duct walls. The total sound power level passing through the duct walls into the receiving room SWL_B is given approximately by

$$SWL_B = SWL_D - R + 10 \log \left(\frac{S_w}{S_D} \right) \text{ dB} \qquad (5.11)$$

where SWL_D is the average sound power level inside the duct, over the length contained in the receiving room, dB

  R is the sound reduction index of the duct wall, dB

  S_w is the total surface area of ducting radiating into the receiving room, m^2

  S_D is the cross sectional area of the duct, m^2.

The value of sound power level calculated from equation 5.11 can then be used to calculate the sound pressure level anywhere in the receiving room using equation (4.17). Note that S_w should include *all* the surface area available to radiate into the room even if the duct is near one or more of the room surfaces. Reflection effects will be taken care of by using the appropriate value of directivity factor in equation (4.17) i.e.

  $Q_\theta = 2$ if duct runs along centre of ceiling

  $Q_\theta = 4$ if duct runs along junction of wall and ceiling.

If values of sound reduction index for sheet metal ducts given in Appendix B are used, equation (5.11), strictly speaking applies to rectangular ducting. It has been found to give reasonable accuracy for circular ducting of the same material, but at low frequencies, it will probably overestimate the amount of sound power breaking out because of the increased stiffness of the circular ducting. It will be immediately obvious that when the term $10 \log (S_w/S_D)$ approaches or exceeds the value of sound reduction index, equation (5.11) indicates either that all the induct sound power SWL_D breaks out, or that more sound power breaks out than was originally in the duct. Under these conditions the assumptions which lead to the derivation of this particular equation are no longer valid, and it cannot be used. When this happens we assume that half the sound power in the duct breaks out, and the rest carries on along the system. In other words, we assume that

$$SWL_B \text{ is never greater than } (SWL_D - 3) \text{ dB}$$

EXAMPLE 5.6

If the sound power level inside a rectangular 20 g steel duct is as shown in the table below, and the dimensions of the duct are 600 mm × 300 mm, calculate the expected sound power level "break out". The length of the duct exposed is 10 m.

Area of duct radiating $= 10 \times (1\cdot2 + \cdot6) \text{ m}^2$
$\qquad\qquad\qquad\qquad = 18 \text{ m}^2$
Cross sectional area $\quad = \cdot6 \times \cdot3 \text{ m}^2$
$\qquad\qquad\qquad\qquad = \cdot18 \text{ m}^2$

$10 \log \dfrac{S_w}{S_D} = 20 \text{ dB}$

Octave Band Centre Freq	Hz	63	125	250	500	1000	2000	4000	8000
SWL$_D$ (given)	dB	74	71	76	75	70	65	58	50
R (Appendix B—20 g steel)	dB	3	8	14	20	26	32	38	40
10 log (S$_w$/S$_D$)	dB	20	20	20	20	20	20	20	20
SWL Breakout (eqn. (5.11))	dB	71	68	73	72	64	53	40	30

Noise due to mechanical vibration

The noise radiated into a particular room due to mechanical vibration of a piece of equipment, like a fan, located elsewhere in a building is not at all easily predicted even approximately. We can, however, eliminate the need for prediction if we ensure that the efficiency of isolation between the fan and its supporting structure is at least 90% at the lowest likely forcing frequency (usually the impeller rotational frequency). Methods of achieving this are discussed fully in Chapter 7.

Cross-talk

Just as noise was readily radiated from a duct termination into a room, so a certain amount of sound energy already in a room can pass into the duct. If this duct is connected via a main duct, to a branch duct leading to another room, then clearly a situation could arise where the noise in the first room was clearly heard in the second. This effect is generally referred to as cross-talk, and is shown diagrammatically in fig. 5.15.

We can regard the system consisting of the duct termination in the source room, the duct termination in the receiving room, and the ducting between, as a "weak" area in the wall separating the two rooms. The problem is to calculate the sound pressure level that will result in the receiving room due to a source of known sound power level in the source room.

The calculation of the amount of energy lost in cross-talk from one room to another is a relatively simple matter. The first thing is to calculate the amount of sound power which will start off at the source end of the duct. We first calculate the sound pressure level next to the outside of the grille or diffuser in the source room. This is obtained directly from equation (4.17).

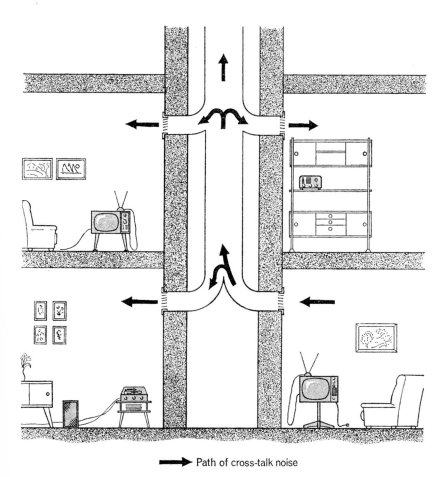

➤ Path of cross-talk noise

Fig. 5.15. "Cross-talk" between rooms

We then assume that the sound pressure just inside the duct will be the same as that outside, less the reflection losses shown in fig. 5.7—these losses applying whichever way the sound is travelling. We then have from equation (3.6), that the sound power level in the end of the duct, is this sound pressure level plus 10 log S, where S is the area of the duct in m². From then on, the procedure for calculating the resulting sound pressure level in the receiving room is exactly the same as that detailed earlier for calculating the transmission of fan noise through the system, except that if the sound energy has to travel via a main duct, there will be additional losses. If the form of the branch is a 90° tee, energy from the branch will travel equally in both directions along the main duct, so assume a 3 dB loss for division. In addition there will be an attenuation due to the bend form approximately equal to that given in fig. 5.5.

For inclined or radiussed branches, the loss will be due to reflection at the sudden expansion. In this case assume a loss of 3 dB at frequencies where wavelengths are equal to or greater than the smallest dimension of the branch duct, and no reflection loss at higher frequencies.

CHAPTER 6

Principles of noise control

Having established our design goal (Chapter 2), and having predicted how much noise will occur (Chapters 4 and 5), we will almost certainly find that the goal can not be achieved without some measure of noise control.

In Chapter 7 we shall be examining practical ways to achieve a required noise reduction. It will be helpful however, if we first look at some of the fundamental principles involved. In this way, we can gain a better understanding of how the noise control techniques work, and, most important, what their limitations may be.

The practical techniques we shall be describing in the next chapter will be found to employ one or more of the following four basic principles:

Sound insulation (Transmission loss)
Sound absorption in rooms and enclosures
Sound absorption in ducts
Vibration isolation.

In this chapter we shall examine the physical mechanisms involved, and in Chapter 7 the applications of these principles.

Sound Insulation

As with thermal, electrical or any other sort of insulation, sound insulation means providing a barrier to the flow of energy—in this case acoustic energy. The most obvious way of doing this is to provide a solid impervious barrier in the path of propagation. What we need to know therefore are the parameters of the barrier which determine how much insulation it will provide.

First let us recapitulate on the mechanism by which sound energy gets into and passes through a solid barrier. We recall that energy reaches the partition in the form of a pressure wave. At the partition the element of air immediately next to the surface is "pressurised" by the arrival of a sound wave. The "pressure" energy it now contains is used in two ways. First it physically moves the surface of the partition, and, second, it compresses the next elemental volume of air in the direction away from the wall. We say then, that of the energy *incident* upon the partition, some passes into the partition and the rest is *reflected*. The reflected energy we have already examined when discussing the behaviour of sound in rooms in Chapter 4, and we shall be discussing its control later in this chapter. Here, we are concerned with the energy which passes into the structure of the partition. This is also used in two ways. First the movement of the partition, however small, involves distortion of its molecular structure. Displacement of molecules relative to each other involves frictional forces, and in overcoming these, part of the sound energy is transformed into heat inside the structure of the partition. We say then, that some of the energy is lost in overcoming the internal damping of the partition—or, some of the energy is *absorbed*. In addition to this, since pressure waves can travel in a solid material by a similar process as sound waves in air (equation (1.1)), some energy will travel along the partition to its ends, and on through other parts of the building structure. We shall be discussing the effects of this later. For the moment it is sufficient to note that this so-called *flanking transmission* is another item in the overall energy balance.

In most cases, both absorbed and flanking energy is small compared with the amount of energy that is left to physically move the surface of the partition on the receiving side, and hence to re-appear as airborne sound. There will be instances however where we have designed the structure to give us very low transmission through the partition, in which case the amount of flanking energy may be the limiting factor. We shall be examining this in more detail later.

The chain of events therefore is airborne sound, to mechanical vibration of the partition, and back to airborne sound on the receiving side, with some of the energy being lost en route by reflection and internal absorption. It is important to realise that when talking of *insulation* we mean the capability of the partition to resist taking in airborne acoustic energy and turning it into vibrational energy. Looking at the energy flow diagram in figure 6.1, we see that if the energy passing into the partition is to be low, the reflected energy must be high, bearing in mind that in most practical constructions the absorbed and flanking energy is small compared with either of the other two forms. Again, recalling the physical mechanism of what happens when a sound wave meets the surface, this requires that the element of pressurised air next to the surface should find it very much easier to expand "backwards" than to move the surface. On that basis we can now interpret "acoustic insulation" as meaning the resistance of the partition to movement under an applied acoustic pressure.

Before examining what determines resistance to movement, we recall that the measure of acoustic insulation is the ratio of the sound energy radiated on the receiving side of the partition, to the sound energy incident upon the source side. This ratio we saw in Chapter 3 was called the sound transmission coefficient, τ, and we defined the decibel representation of it, the sound reduction index, in equation (3.10) by

$$R = 10 \log \left(\frac{1}{\tau} \right) \text{ dB} \tag{6.1}$$

When referring then to insulation, or resistance to movement, we mean sound reduction index.

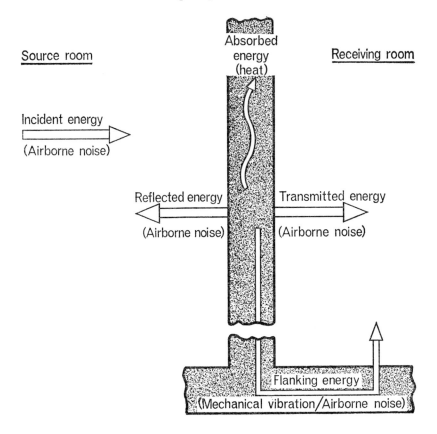

Fig. 6.1. Energy flow in an acoustically excited partition

Single partition

(a) The effect of mass and frequency

Now, what qualities of a partition determine its resistance to movement? One of the most important is mass. If we try to vibrate the partition rapidly, its resistance to movement is governed largely by the inertia force which acts in the opposite direction to the applied force. The higher the mass, the greater is the inertia force resisting movement, hence the higher is the sound reduction index. The frequency of the applied force is also important. If we try to move a given mass more times per second, the velocity of movement must be correspondingly higher, as must be the resulting inertia forces, and hence the sound reduction index will again be higher.

The combined effects of mass and frequency can be analysed theoretically for a single leaf panel to result in what is commonly referred to

I

as the "mass law of sound insulation", i.e.:

$$R = 20 \log Mf - 43 \text{ dB} \qquad (6.2)$$

Where M is the superficial weight of the partition, kg/m²
f is the frequency, Hz.

Equation (6.2) as it stands applies strictly to the particular case where the sound is impinging onto the surface in the form of plane waves which are parallel to the surface—that is, incident at 0°. If the source side is a semi-reverberant room however, as is more usually the case, the sound will be impinging on the panel from all directions. Under these conditions the sound reduction index will be rather less than that predicted by the normal incidence mass law. Provided the range of angles of incidence is less than about 80° on either side of the normal to the partition, we normally use the "field incidence" law, which has the same form as the normal incidence mass law, but is about 6 dB lower. If there is much sound likely to be incident on the partition at, or near, grazing incidence, 80° to 90°, which might occur for example if the source side is a highly reverberant room, neither the field incidence law nor the normal incidence law, as expressed in equation (6.2) will apply—the level at any value of M.f being lower, and also doubling mass or frequency gives only 5 dB

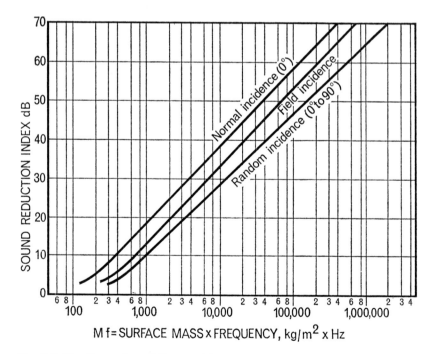

Fig. 6.2. The "mass laws" for partitions

increase in sound reduction index, compared with the 6dB increase predicted in equation (6.2). The three curves are shown in figure 6.2. Weights of some common building materials are given in Table 6.1.

(b) The effect of stiffness

(i) Resonance

While the various representations of the mass law undoubtedly provide a useful guide to sound reduction, we must not forget that it is a theoretical prediction. One of the fundamental assumptions made, is that the partition is heavy and limp—that is, it has very low stiffness. A real partition has of course some degree of stiffness. If we move it very slowly (low frequency) then its resistance to movement is governed entirely by its stiffness. The inertia forces associated with its mass are relatively small because the velocity of movement is small, and it is only the inherent "springiness" of the partition which resists movement. Under these conditions we say the sound reduction index is "stiffness controlled". Stiffness in a structure also has the unfortunate characteristic of producing resonance. If we strike a sharp blow, or hold it in some displaced position and suddenly release it, it will oscillate for a time at its own "natural" frequency. If we now force it with sound waves at that frequency, it will obviously move with much greater amplitude than if forced at any other frequency. Hence the sound reduction index will be very much lower. In fact, most partitions have a number of natural frequencies, the lowest

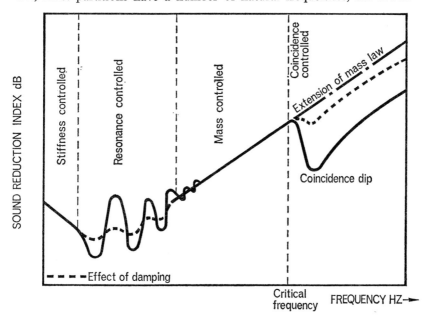

Fig. 6.3. Characteristic transmission loss of a partition

frequency being referred to as the "fundamental". The others are usually close to this and just above it in frequency, and have progressively decreasing amplitude. If we now modify the mass law curve at the low frequency end of the spectrum, we might expect a typical form as shown in figure 6.3.

(ii) *Coincidence*

Figure 6.3 shows another peculiar (and unfortunate) effect of stiffness—the effect of coincidence. If we vibrate a panel in a direction normal to its surface, a bending wave will travel along the panel rather like the waves in a shaken sheet. This means that at any instant the panel will have a corrugated form as shown exaggerated in figure 6.4. Any point on the panel will be oscillating in a direction normal to the plane of the panel as the bending wave passes along. If we had a series of sound waves striking the panel at some oblique angle, it is not too difficult to see that the situation could arise where the projected wavelength of the oncoming sound was exactly equal to the length of the bending wave in the panel. Then we would have a region of high pressure for example running along the panel at the same speed as the bending wave, so that it is always next

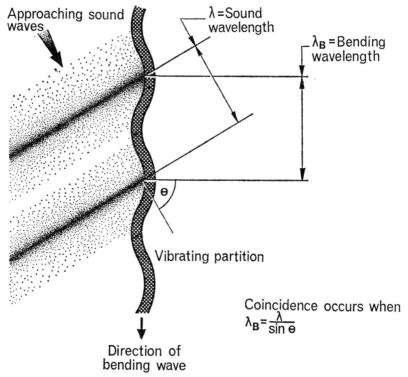

Approaching sound waves

λ =Sound wavelength

λ_B =Bending wavelength

θ

Vibrating partition

Direction of bending wave

Coincidence occurs when $\lambda_B = \dfrac{\lambda}{\sin \theta}$

Fig. 6.4. The coincidence effect

to the region of the panel having the highest displacement. The effect is similar to that of low frequency resonance, and the sound reduction again falls below the mass law prediction.

The unfortunate thing about coincidence is that it is not a single frequency phenomenon. The velocity at which bending waves travel along a partition increases with frequency. We call the frequency at which a bending wave will travel in a partition at the same velocity as sound travels in air, the *critical frequency*. Approximate values of critical frequency for some common materials, are given in Table 6.1. Obviously, the only sound waves at this frequency which will coincide with the bending wave in the partition are those which travel along the partition at grazing incidence (90°). At higher frequencies the length of the bending wave is higher than the length of the sound wave, so there will always be some angle of incidence at which the projected wavelength of the sound is exactly equal to the bending wavelength. The nett result is that above the critical frequency, the sound reduction index will stay below the mass law prediction rather as indicated in figure 6.3.

The effects of stiffness then are generally undesirable. The low frequency effect is not too much of a problem—resonant frequency being generally less than 100 Hz for most practical constructions used in building. Coincidence however is a problem because it often results in a loss of insulation in the mid to high frequency region. Figure 6.5 is a summary of the results of measurements on a large number of partitions carried out by the National Physical Laboratory. Clearly illustrated here is the detrimental effect of coincidence on most materials likely to be found in common use.

We come to the conclusion therefore, that for high sound reduction index over a wide frequency range, the requirement is for high mass and low stiffness.

TABLE 6.1
Critical frequencies and surface densities of some common materials

Material	Critical frequency $\times$ surface density $Hz \times kg\ m^{-2}$	Surface density per unit thickness $kg\ m^{-2}\ mm^{-1}$
Lead	600,000	11.2
Partition board	124,000	1·6
Steel	97,700	8·1
Reinforced concrete	44,000	2·3
Brick	42,000	1·9
Glass	39,000	2·5
Perspex	35,500	1·15
Asbestos cement	33,600	1·9
Aluminium	32,200	2·7
Hardboard	30,600	0·81
Plasterboard	32,000	0·75
Flaxboard	13,200	0·39
Plywood	13,000	0·58

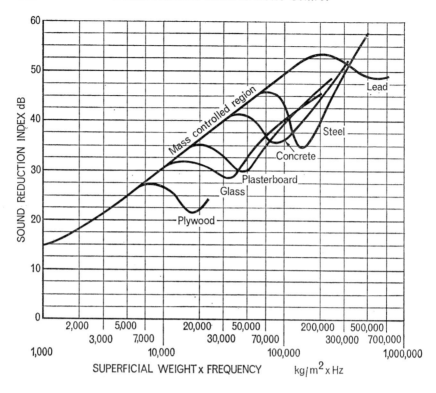

Fig. 6.5. Sound reduction index for common building materials

(iii) *Damping*

We may find that we have a panel which has sufficient mass to give good insulation, but the full potential is not being realised because high stiffness is narrowing the frequency range between resonance and coincidence (fig. 6.3). Lowering the stiffness of an existing panel is not usually possible, but we can sometimes reduce the effects of stiffness by increasing the damping in the partition.

The effect of damping on the behaviour of the partition is felt most at the resonance and the coincidence frequencies. We have seen that when either of these conditions occur, the movement of the panel is exactly in phase with the arrival of each sound wave. Partitions which have high damping inherent in their material will obviously offer more resistance to this sort of "free" vibration and the more resistance they offer, the greater is the proportion of energy which is absorbed and turned into heat in overcoming the internal friction forces associated with damping. Consequently the amplitude of the "dips" in the transmission loss curve (fig. 6.3) would be lower for partitions of highly damped material. Note in figure 6.3 that damping is only effective in the frequency ranges where resonance and coincidence occurs. There is virtually no effect on sound reduction index due to damping, in the frequency range where the mass law applies.

The conclusion we come to then, is that while we cannot extend the frequency range between resonance and coincidence, we can, by adding damping to the partition, reduce the losses in these regions. The most common method of adding damping to a partition is to apply to one side of the partition, a layer of mastic-like material having high hysteresis losses. If this layer has a good bond to the surface of the partition, energy used to displace the partition will now have to deform the damping compound as well. Consequently a much larger proportion is transformed into heat inside the damping layer itself. Types of material that can be used are discussed in more detail in Chapter 7.

Needless to say, this type of treatment will be effective only on partitions that have very low damping themselves. The higher the damping inherent in the basic structure, the smaller will be the benefit from added damping— it would be pointless to add a damping layer to a masonry partition for example. On the other hand the performance of metal partitions like steel or aluminium sheet, can be greatly improved by this treatment.

Double leaf partitions

Providing we take adequate precautions to minimise the effects of stiffness, we see that we can improve the insulation of a single leaf partition by adding mass—but this can continue only up to a certain point. If for example we are trying to improve upon the insulation of a proposed lightweight office partition weighing say 50 kg/m², we will obviously get worthwhile improvement by replacing it with a 115 mm thick brick wall weighing 200 kg/m²—probably about 10 dB, and in certain circumstances this would justify the cost and weight penalty involved. If on the other hand we already had the brick wall, and were looking for the same order of improvement, making the brick wall four times as thick would almost certainly be prohibitive.

The most obvious solution is to construct a second wall completely separated from the first. It may be thought at first that then we repeat the process of losing energy from the incident sound waves all over again. In other words, if one wall gives us a 40 dB sound reduction index at a particular frequency, two walls must provide 80 dB. The short answer is that they do not. If the two walls were ideally separated (no common footings or edge supports, and no ties), and the air space between them was very large (of the order of a metre or more) then we would achieve something like the arithmetic sum of the sound reduction index of each.

Real walls of course meet neither of these conditions. They have to have common supports at the edges, and probably support from each other, and practical building space limitations rarely allow a cavity between them of more than a few centimetres. Consider what happens with one of the simplest types of double leaf partitions, say 12 mm sheets of plasterboard on either side of 100 mm studding.

Energy enters the panel on the source side in the same way as it did in the single leaf partition. The essential difference is however, that the panel of the double leaf partition does not respond in quite the same way. Instead of having free air to work against on the receiving side, it now has to compress the air trapped between itself and the panel on the receiving side. Compressing this air turns out to be a relatively efficient way of "mechanically" exciting the panel on the receiving side. In other words the transfer of energy across the two panels is rather more efficient than it would be if the two panels had a large distance between them. As if this were not enough, mechanical energy in the vibrating panel on the source side is transmitted very efficiently through the studs, to drive the panel on the receiving side, as indicated in figure 6.6.

The nett result is that far from getting double the sound reduction index of one panel, one ends up with an improvement of only about 10 dB

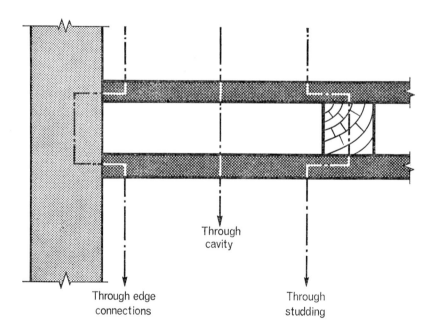

Through
cavity

Through edge
connections

Through
studding

Fig. 6.6. Flanking transmission in stud partitions

at mid to high frequencies, and virtually no improvement at low frequencies, over a single panel construction of equal weight.

The performance of this type of partition can be reduced further by resonances of the air in the cavity itself—first lower frequencies associated with the height and width, and then by higher frequencies associated with the thickness of the airspace. These are not normally a problem however, as they are easily overcome simply by fixing a blanket of absorptive material in the cavity. This need not fill the cavity completely—the frequencies concerned being such that a 50 mm thick blanket will usually suffice.

Sound absorption in rooms

We saw in the discussion on the behaviour of sound in rooms (Chapter 4) that the reverberant sound pressure level resulting from a source of given sound power level was dependent upon the average absorption coefficient in the room (equation 4.17). The average absorption coefficient in turn depended upon the individual absorption coefficients of the various room surfaces (equation 4.12). The questions we now discuss are what characteristics of a surface determine its absorption properties, and how do we increase an absorption coefficient?

To return yet again to what happens when sound waves meet solid barrier partitions, we recall that when the layer of air next to a partition was compressed by the oncoming wave, part of its energy was expended in moving the partition, and the rest propagated away from the wall as a "backward" travelling sound wave—the rest in fact was reflected. To give some idea of the orders of magnitude involved, looking at the energy balance in figure 6.1, if the sound were at 125 Hz and the wall had a very hard non porous surface, probably as much as 99 per cent of the energy in the incident wave would be reflected, leaving about 1 per cent to enter the partition structure. As a matter of interest, if the sound reduction index were 30 dB, only a tenth of this 1 per cent would eventually be re-radiated as sound on the other side.

In the previous section we were concerned with the 1 per cent. Here we are concerned with the 99 per cent, and how to reduce it, without, and this is of fundamental importance, increasing the 1 per cent. In fact, the principle of sound absorption, just as its name implies, is to reduce the amount of reflected energy by transforming it into some form of energy other than vibrational energy.

An obvious alternative form of energy is heat. When we were discussing earlier in this chapter the behaviour of the energy once it had entered the wall, we noted that some of it was turned into heat by the internal damping of the wall structure (fig. 6.1). In fact, this is "absorption" in the same context that we are discussing now—except that here, we need to produce this effect in the air immediately next to the partition on the source side. We shall now examine the more common ways in which it can be achieved.

Porous absorbers

One mechanism by which heat can be generated is by movement against frictional forces. To produce a region of high frictional resistance to air movement, we fill the space next to the partition with a blanket of fairly loose fibrous or cellular material. As the sound waves move through this, the relatively small pores or interstices between fibres in the material present passages of high frictional loss to the small displacement of air as the pressure waves pass by. Hence energy is progressively removed from the wave as it passes through the absorption material, the nett result being that less sound energy emerges from the blanket after reflection from the back wall (the partition) than originally entered it—the difference having been transformed into heat energy inside the material.

Now we need to be a little more precise in the specification of a suitable material, so let us examine the properties on which the amount of energy absorbed will depend. In the first place the energy must obviously be able to get into the material. A material which was so rigid and impervious that the wave could not enter the pores or interstices, would simply reflect most of the energy as the partition did. Therefore it must be sufficiently open and loosely packed to allow the wave in. Also, once in, there must be sufficient friction in the material to absorb energy. If the material is too open or lightly packed, the wave travels through relatively easily, without much loss of energy.

The two factors which have most bearing on a material's capacity to absorb sound are *porosity* and *flow resistance*. Porosity is the fraction of unit volume of the material which is taken up by the air contained in that volume. Provided it is over about 75 per cent, variations from one material to another, do not have a large effect upon absorption coefficient, except perhaps at high frequencies where a less porous material will start to reflect sound from solid areas of its surface. Flow resistance is a measure of the ease with which an airflow can pass through the material. It is in fact determined experimentally in just that way, as shown in figure 6.7. The pressure drop, Δp in N/m^2, across a sample of thickness d in m, is measured at the same time as the velocity of air through the sample, v m/sec. With these units, the flow resistance is then defined as

$$R_f = \frac{\Delta p}{d.v} \quad \text{mks Rayls/m} \tag{6.1}$$

(Yet another symbol R, but fortunately any combination with room constant or sound reduction index is most unlikely.)

The value of flow resistance expressed by equation (6.1) is of course for "d.c." flow, while acoustic waves are "a.c.", but at least at low frequency where most of our problems occur, it also represents the dynamic value fairly well. Again, provided the value of flow resistance is in excess of about 10^4 Rayls, fairly wide variations do not seem to have a drastic effect upon absorption coefficient, at least up to values around 10^6 Rayls.

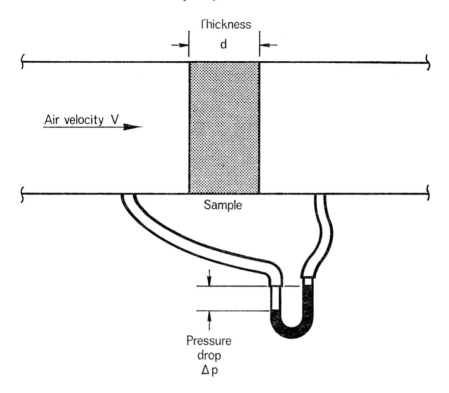

Fig. 6.7. Measurement of flow resistance

Once we have a material which will allow the sound energy to enter without much reflection, but at the same time provide sufficient resistance to absorb energy during transmission, we have to decide how it is to be arranged on the surface and in what quantities. As far as quantity is concerned, a general rule is, the more absorption in the room we need, the greater is the room surface area that should be covered with absorptive material. That leaves thickness, and method of mounting to be decided, and here we have to consider again for a moment the mechanism of absorption.

We have seen that the transformation of kinetic energy in the sound wave into heat energy is achieved by doing work against frictional resistance. Obviously the faster the rate of doing work, the greater will be the absorption of energy per unit time—or, power absorbed. This means of course that the material should occupy the region of air near the partition where acoustic velocities of the air molecules are highest. If we plot the variation of acoustic particle velocity with distance from the partition, for the case of a single frequency sound, the result will look rather like the curve shown in figure 6.8.

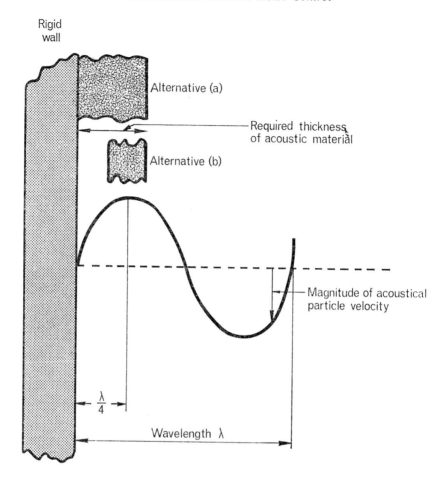

Fig. 6.8. Importance of thickness of absorptive material

Immediately at the surface of the partition, the particle velocity is zero—
or at least very small (there must be some movement of the surface, or
the sound reduction index would be infinite!) As we move away, we find
the velocity increasing until it reaches a maximum at a point which is at a
distance from the surface equal to one quarter of the wavelength of the
sound. If we cover the partition with material having a thickness less
than one quarter of the wavelength, then clearly we are not absorbing
that sound in the most efficient manner possible. To ensure that we do,
we must make the thickness equal to or greater than a quarter-wavelength.
Since the wavelength of the sound is inversely proportional to the
frequency of the sound (equation (6.2)) this means that the maximum
thickness of absorptive material is determined by the lowest frequency
sound we wish to absorb. For high absorption, say 90 per cent down to

say 250 Hz, this implies we need a blanket about 300 mm thick. Unfortunately this is true, although we can still get very useful absorption at that level of frequency even with 100 mm thick material.

We can do even better if we space the blanket away from the wall to give an overall thickness of say 200 mm. As a general rule, a given overall thickness has the same effect whether it is made up of solid material, or of material plus airspace.

We can summarise the behaviour of porous absorbers by saying that, providing porosity and flow resistance are in the right range, the characteristic shape of the absorption-frequency curve is as shown in figure 6.9. Low frequency response is generally poor, but absorption does rise to a maximum, generally above 0·8 at mid to high frequencies. There may be a slight decrease at high frequencies if porosity is low. The effect of increasing thickness of the material or adding an airspace behind it, is to lower the frequency at which the high values of absorption start to fall off. This "cut-off" frequency is that whose wavelength in air is roughly four times the overall thickness of the material, or the material plus airspace.

Single resonant absorbers

The simplest example of a resonant absorber is a vessel, such as a bottle, containing only air, and connected to the outside by a narrow tunnel similar to the neck of a bottle. The air in the tunnel is effectively a small mass, and the air contained in the volume of the bottle behaves like a spring. If we pressurise the inside of the vessel and suddenly release the pressure, we would find that the mass of air in the tunnel would oscillate

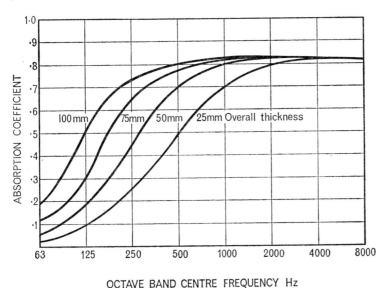

Fig. 6.9. Typical absorption characteristics of porous blanket material

backwards and forwards at its natural frequency, or at the *resonant* frequency of the vessel. Now because this "plug" of air is moving in a relatively small passage (the tunnel), the "spring" (volume of air in the vessel) will have to expend some energy in overcoming the frictional resistance. The greater the amplitude of oscillation the more energy is lost in overcoming friction. The resonant frequency of a "cavity" resonant absorber, or Helmholtz resonator as they are sometimes called, can be predicted from

$$f_{RES} = 55 \sqrt{\frac{S}{lV}} \ Hz \tag{6.2}$$

where S is the cross sectional area of the tunnel or neck, m²
    l is the length of the neck, m
    V is the volume of air enclosed in the vessel, m³.

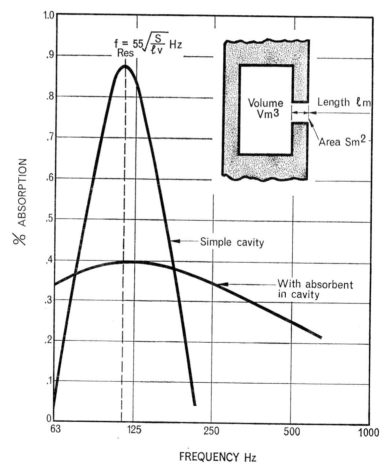

Fig. 6.10. Typical absorption characteristic of a resonant absorber

If the "plug" is now excited continuously by a succession of sound waves arriving at the same frequency as the resonant frequency, it is not difficult to imagine that the amplitude of the plug will be very large indeed, and a considerable amount of energy can be extracted from each wave in this manner. In fact it is possible to achieve absorption coefficients as high as 0·90 at the resonant frequency. Unfortunately the amplitude of vibration, and hence power absorbed, falls off rapidly if the resonator is excited at a frequency either just above or just below the resonant frequency (see fig. 6.10).

For this reason the single resonator has fairly limited applications, e.g. enclosures for machines emitting noise at one constant frequency. They can be used in rooms in the form of arrays of resonators of slightly differing dimensions, where a fairly restricted range of low frequency absorption is required. Then it is usual to fill the cavity with some form of porous material, which has the effect of broadening the frequency response curve, but also unfortunately lowering the peak absorption coefficient.

Multiple resonant absorbers

If one reduces the peak absorption of a resonator by attempting to broaden its frequency response with porous material in the cavity as a damper, one requires of course a greater number of resonators to get the same total absorption (Sα—see equation (4.12)). As an alternative to using many individual resonators, it is possible to get the same effect by placing a sheet of perforated metal, or board some distance away from the surface of the partition. Each hole and the volume of air immediately behind it acts like the neck and volume respectively of an individual resonator. In fact it is not necessary to provide partitions between the holes at all (fig. 6.11). Again a broad frequency response requires the use of an absorptive blanket in the airspace, but the loss of efficiency does not seem so drastic as with a single resonator.

The frequency of maximum absorption, at which the absorption coefficient could be in the region of 0·8, is given approximately by

$$f_{RES} = 5000 \sqrt{\frac{p}{l(t + 0·8d)}} \text{ Hz} \qquad (6.3)$$

where p is the percentage open area of the panel
    l is the depth of the airspace, mm
    t is the thickness of the panel, mm
    d is the diameter of the holes, mm.

By suitable combination therefore of large, well spaced holes, thick panels, and large depth of airspace, it is possible to achieve much higher absorption at low frequencies than would be possible by the porous material alone. At the same time mid-frequency absorption will be provided by the absorptive material, up to the point where sound is

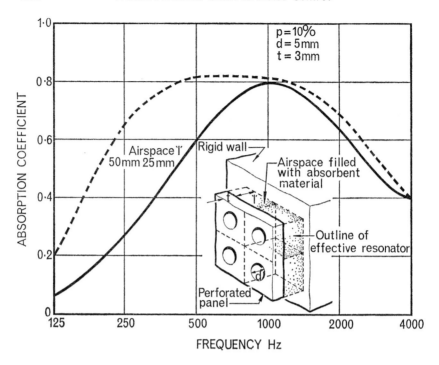

Fig. 6.11. Typical performance of a multiple resonant absorber

reflected by the impervious material between the holes in the panel.

Large numbers of holes designed to offset the high frequency loss, will, by and large, reduce the resonant effect of the panel. Eventually a large enough percentage open area will give no more benefit than the inherent absorptive properties of the porous blanket by itself—the panel then serving only as a decorative support for the blanket. As a rough guide, the changeover from marked resonant performance, to simple porous blanket performance lies in the 20 to 30 per cent open area range.

Panel or membrane absorbers

All the absorbers we have examined so far have produced the transformation from kinetic energy to heat energy by forcing air to move against frictional forces in narrow passages. We have already seen earlier in the chapter that it is also possible to achieve this transformation by deforming a solid panel. One type of absorber therefore relies upon the sound waves having to do work on a panel of high internal damping material before they reach the surface of the main partition. An example of the so called panel, or membrane absorber is shown in figure 6.12, together with a typical frequency response curve.

As with the resonant absorber the greater the amplitude of movement—in this case of the panel—the greater is the energy lost in overcoming its internal friction. The panel, the airspace behind it, and its support, is just another mass spring system, and as we might expect, has a resonant frequency of its own. Also as we might expect, the amount of energy it extracts from the sound field is highest when the frequency of the sound coincides with its own resonant frequency. This depends on the stiffness of the panel airspace combination and on the weight of the panel. For flexible sheets like plywood or hardboard, the resonant frequency is given approximately by

$$f_{RES} = 60\sqrt{\frac{1}{ml}} \, Hz \qquad (6.4)$$

where m is the superficial weight of the panel, kg/m²
    l is the depth of the airspace, m

Again the addition of damping, in the form of porous blanket in the airspace for example, broadens the response curve.

A point often overlooked is that free standing panels of fairly large area, like windows, act also as absorbers. The main difference is that besides being determined by their mass, the response is dependent upon their inherent stiffness only—there being no airspace behind to act like a spring.

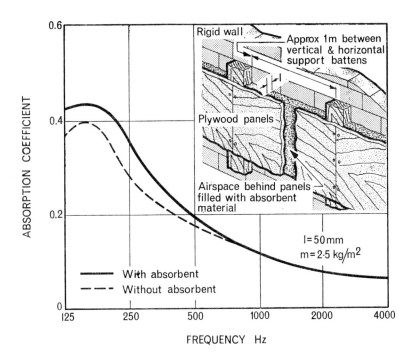

Fig. 6.12. Typical performance of plywood panel absorber

K

Sound absorption in ducts

Ducts containing a flow of acoustic energy, with or without air or other gas flow, warrant special examination. Unlike a large room or enclosure, the space contained in a duct does not contain a reverberant sound field as such—most of the energy in the sound waves being carried in a direction parallel to the duct axis. There are often high frequency waves present which travel across the duct, or more generally in some direction inclined to the axis, progressing along the duct by repeated reflections from the walls. Except in some special cases however these carry only a small proportion of the total energy present, and in any case lose energy fairly quickly from the large number of reflections.

The waves that cause most trouble are the so-called plane waves, which as their name suggests travel as "flat" planes, just as the waves from the piston in the model used in Chapter 1.

In Chapter 5, we discussed one method of achieving absorption in a duct run, and that was by allowing the duct wall to vibrate (fig. 5.3). In fact the wall acted as a panel absorber. The attenuation achieved in this manner however was generally small, at best about 0·3 to 0·6 dB per metre run.

As we have seen, porous absorptive material works very well—what will happen then if we fix this to the inside surfaces of the duct? The plane wave will start off in the lined section as in an unlined duct, but as it travels on, energy is progressively lost at the edges of the wave which pass through the absorptive lining, in exactly the same way as we have discussed previously. Also, for lower frequencies the velocity of sound in most porous materials is lower than in air. We therefore get a "bending" effect rather as shown in figure 6.13.

The result is that energy is continually being extracted from the portion of the wave which is travelling in air. In other words the "decay" of energy is higher than it would be if the duct were unlined. How much greater? It can be shown that the amount of energy extracted per unit length of lined duct is proportional to the absorption coefficient of the

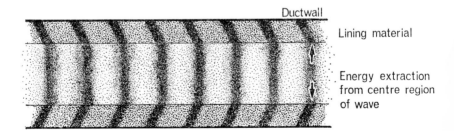

Ductwall

Lining material

Energy extraction from centre region of wave

Fig. 6.13. Dissipation of energy at ends of plane waves in a lined duct

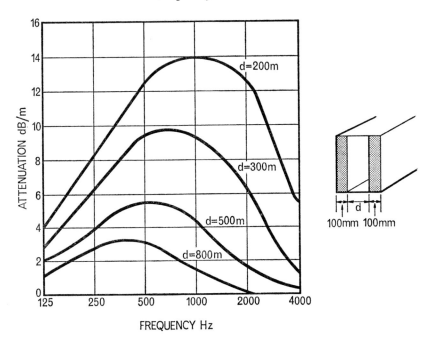

Fig. 6.14. Attenuation in ducts lined with 100mm thick rockwool blanket
nominal density 80 kg/m³ and airspace d

lining, and to the ratio P/S, where P is the perimeter of the lining, and S
is the nett cross sectional area of the duct. The dependence upon this
particular ratio is very interesting. In the first place it tells us that for high
attenuation we must try to maximise the ratio. If we examine its value for
some representative shapes, we will find that,

$$\text{For a circular duct,} \quad \frac{P}{S} = \frac{4}{\text{diameter}}$$

$$\text{For a square duct,} \quad \frac{P}{S} = \frac{4}{\text{side}}$$

$$\text{For a rectangular duct } (h \times d), \quad \frac{P}{S} = \frac{2(h+d)}{hd}$$

A circular and a square duct of comparable size will therefore provide
much the same attenuation. In the case of the rectangular duct however,
we see that if we can choose dimensions such that the height h is much
larger than the width d, the ratio P/S approximates to 1/d. In other words
we can maximise the attenuation by passing the sound through a duct
whose width is much smaller than its height, and the smaller we make
the width the higher is the attenuation. This is illustrated graphically in
figure 6.14 for the particular case of a duct lined with 100mm rockwool.

Practical ways of achieving high attenuation with low flow resistance are discussed in the next chapter. The shape of the curves in figure 6.13 are quite characteristic for lined ducts. At low frequencies there is a drop in attenuation because of the dependence upon the absorption characteristics of the material. As we saw in the earlier discussion on absorption in rooms, this is limited by the thickness of the material. If we want to increase low frequency attenuation, we have to use correspondingly thicker lining material.

At high frequencies, attenuation falls off for a rather different reason. High frequency waves carry most energy in the region near the centre of the duct. This means that the energy absorbing mechanism of the lining is not having much effect on the overall energy content of the wave, and it tends to carry on as if the lining were not present. This effect is most pronounced when the wavelength becomes comparable with or less than the width of the duct.

Bends

We saw in Chapter 5 that a plain untreated bend, will attenuate sound energy by a process of reflection. We also noted (fig. 5.5) that for frequencies where wavelength was higher or lower than about half the duct width, the energy passed through the bend relatively easily. This is because when the inside end of a plane wave coming into the bend actually reaches the corner, it cannot travel on across the end of the outgoing leg of the bend in "free space" as it were. As we saw in the case of a barrier (Chapter 4) the wave diffracts around the corner, and starts to propagate along the outgoing leg. At first the direction of propagation is in direction inclined to the duct axis as well as along it. Waves inclined to the axis however are eventually damped out and only the plane wave is left.

We can accelerate the decay of the waves inclined to the axis, however, if we line the outgoing leg with a suitably absorptive material as described above for plain ducts. This also has an effect on the mid to high frequency waves which start out from the bend as plane waves. In fact we can do even better by also lining the leg into the bend, which has the effect of ensuring that any waves inclined to the axis which may be present, are removed before they reach the corner. The nett effect is shown in figure 6.15 and comparison with the attenuation afforded by the plain bend (fig. 5.5) shows the benefit that can be gained.

Vibration isolation

When we spoke earlier of acoustic insulation, we took this to mean a barrier to the flow of acoustic energy from one point to another. In that sense vibration isolation might very well be called vibration "insulation". All it means is the provision of a barrier to the flow of *vibrational* energy from one point to another. In the acoustic case we were concerned with energy in the form of pressure waves in the air. In the case of vibration,

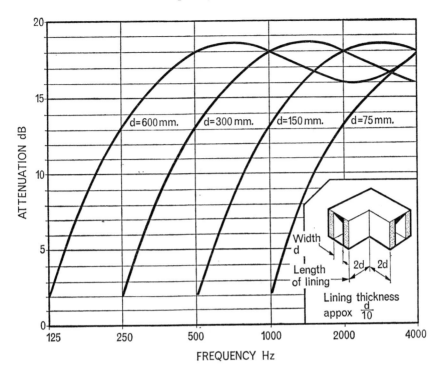

Fig. 6.15. Attenuation from lined bends

we can think of the energy in terms of "force" waves in a solid structure. Consider the simple case of a rotating machine bolted originally to a solid foundation. Any residual out-of-balance force in the rotating parts could be represented as a weight located eccentrically as indicated in figure 6.16 (a). Obviously as the weight rotates each part of the machine structure will be subjected to a cyclic force, due to the inertia of the rotating off-centre weight. As far as the vertical component of the force is concerned (usually the most important), this will appear to be acting alternately upwards and downwards, at a frequency equal to the shaft rotational frequency. While all machine structures have a certain degree of flexibility in them, we can assume for the moment that our machine is sufficiently rigid for every point on its structure to experience the same vertical component of out-of-balance force at the same instant. This of course includes the bottom faces of the mounting feet.

This is perhaps an appropriate point to mention that residual out-of-balance force in a rotating machine is of course only one mechanism by which fluctuating load can be exerted on the foundation. Combustion loads in reciprocating engines, magnetostrictive forces in electrical machines, frictional forces from bearings and sliding components, are all equally (possibly more) common. We shall continue with the out-of-balance

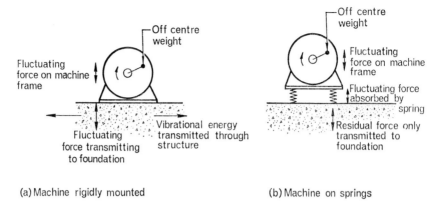

(a) Machine rigidly mounted   (b) Machine on springs

Fig. 6.16. Effect of vibration isolators

example for its simplicity, but it is important to realise that all these other mechanisms can have the same effect.

Now, if the material of the foundation has about the same rigidity as the foot of the machine, obviously the fluctuating force is transmitted very effectively to the foundation, and it deflects. From that point on, the vibrational energy in the foundation may travel very efficiently away from the point of application (the machine foot), into other parts of the building structure and eventually appear as noise energy. From the moment the energy gets into the foundation it behaves much the same as if it had been excited by airborne sound waves (see "Sound Insulation").

How then do we prevent this efficient transmission between machine and foundation? The answer is that we need a device, the top side of which will yield to the force exerted on it by the machine foot, but which is sufficiently flexible to prevent the applied force being felt at the lower side— the side resting on the foundation—before the direction of the applied force is reversed. (At the same time of course, it must be able to withstand the static weight of the machine). In other words we need a vibration isolator.

Undamped Vibration

Perhaps the simplest type of vibration isolator in common use is the steel spring. Consider what happens if we now place a spring between our machine and the foundation as indicated in figure 6.15 (b). The first thing we notice is that the machine settles under its own weight and deflects the spring by a certain amount. This *static deflection* of the isolator usually denoted by δ, is a very important parameter in determining the eventual performance of the spring as an isolator when the machine is running. It depends only upon the static *stiffness* of the spring, and upon the weight of the machine.

If we now lean on the machine to deflect the spring a little more, and then suddenly release it, we will find that the machine will oscillate vertically about its rest position, at one specific frequency. This frequency is called the *natural frequency* of the isolator, and it too depends only upon the static stiffness of the spring, and upon the weight of the machine. In fact, as one might suspect, there is a well defined relationship between the natural frequency of an isolator, and the static deflection of the system, i.e.

$$f_0 = \frac{15 \cdot 8}{\sqrt{\delta}} \text{ Hz} \tag{6.6}$$

where f_0 is the natural frequency of the spring and weight combination, Hz
δ is the static deflection of the spring under the weight of the machine, mm.

Equation (6.6) is represented graphically in figure 6.17.

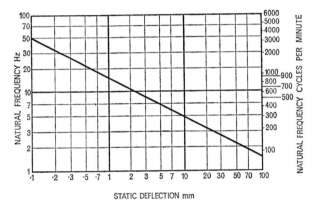

STATIC DEFLECTION mm

Fig. 6.17. Effect of static deflection on natural frequency

When the machine is running at some fixed speed a measure of the performance of the spring as an isolator is the force *transmissibility* defined as:

$$\text{Transmissibility} = \frac{\text{Force transmitted to the foundation}}{\text{Force applied by the machine}} \tag{6.7}$$

If the system is very lightly damped (damping is discussed later), it can be shown that the force transmissibility can be represented by

$$\text{Transmissibility} = \frac{1}{1 - \left(\dfrac{f}{f_0}\right)^2} \tag{6.8}$$

Where f is the frequency of the driving force, H_z
f_0 is the natural frequency of the system, H_z.

Transmissibility is usually expressed as a percentage and the efficiency of the isolation is then 100 minus this.

If we now start the machine and run it up slowly to its operating speed, we can see how the transmissibility varies according to the forcing frequency (machine speed). At rest, of course, the transmissibility is 1, i.e. the force transmitted to the foundation is equal to the weight of the machine. At low rotational speed, f is less than f_0, the natural frequency, and as equation (6.8) shows, the transmitted force is greater than the applied force. The situation continues to deteriorate up to the point where the speed is such that the driving frequency is equal to the natural frequency. Then the transmitted force is infinitely large—in theory anyway— as is the amplitude of the machine on its mounts. In practice of course, displacement is usually restricted by the physical restraints of the system, but when this state of *resonance* as it is called occurs, both amplitude of vibration and transmitted forces become very large.

As speed is increased further, the denominator of equation (6.8) changes sign and again becomes numerically greater than zero. The negative sign means merely that the instantaneous direction of the transmitted force is opposite to that of the applied force. At a driving speed whose frequency is exactly $\sqrt{2}$ times the natural frequency, the transmitted force is again equal to the applied force (not, this time, the static weight of the machine, but the dynamic amplitude of, in the example we have chosen, the out-of-balance force). At speeds higher than this the transmissibility falls below 1, and we start to get isolation.

This characteristic behaviour of vibration isolators can be easily demonstrated by a simple experiment. Join six or eight ordinary elastic bands together to form an elastic rope about 0·3 m long, and attach to one end an object like a heavy ruler weighing about 0·2 Kg. Hold the free end so that the object is allowed to hang vertically below the hand. This then represents a simple mass-spring system of the type we have been discussing.

If the object is pulled downwards and then released it will oscillate vertically at the natural frequency of the system—probably $1\frac{1}{2}$ Hz. When it is again at rest, start to move the hand upwards and downwards smoothly and slowly. (This is not quite the same as applying an oscillating force to the object on a solid foundation, as we have been considering, but the resulting behaviour of a mass resiliently mounted on a moving foundation is precisely the same. We can in fact refer to displacement transmissibility exactly as we do to force transmissibility).

With very slow (about $\frac{1}{2}$ Hz) movements of the hand, it will be found that the elastic "rope" behaves almost as if it were rigid, with the object following the same motion as the hand—i.e. the transmissibility is nearly 1. As the frequency of hand movement is increased, it will be noticed that at the end of a downward movement, when an upward movement starts, the object will continue to move down for a moment due to the inertia of its own weight, before it too starts moving upwards—and vice versa at the end of an upward hand movement. In other words the amplitude transmissibility of the system is increasing, and for the same displacement of the hand we get a greater displacement of the object.

If the frequency of hand movements is increased a little further, until it coincides with the previously observed natural frequency, a state of resonance will be obvious—the object will move up and down with very large amplitude of motion, and it will be possible to maintain this situation with very little effort of the hand.

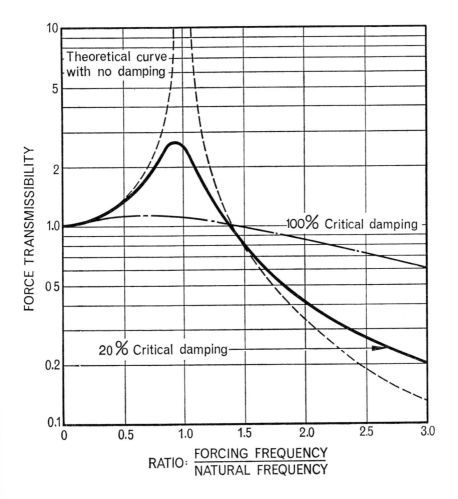

Fig. 6.18. Force transmissibility curves for a simple mass-spring isolator

Moving the hand very rapidly now, will demonstrate true isolation. If the frequency of hand movement is very much higher than the natural frequency, it will be found possible to execute quite large amplitude of hand movements with practically no vertical movement of the object at all. A summary of this behaviour of a simple mass-spring system, is shown in figure 6.18, by the "no damping" curve.

Since transmissibility, and hence efficiency of isolation, at any driving frequency is a function of the natural frequency of the system (equation (6.8)), which is in turn dependent upon static deflection (equation (6.6)), we can by combining the two equations, say immediately what the efficiency of a simple isolator will be, if we know the static deflection. The performance is summarised in figure 6.19.

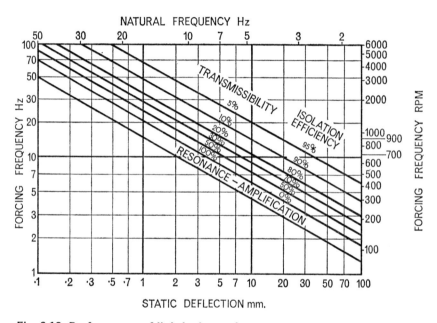

Fig. 6.19. Performance of lightly damped mounts

Damped Vibration

The simple spring isolators we have been considering so far, theoretically have no damping in them at all. That is to say, if we deflected the weight they carried and released it suddenly, the weight would continue to oscillate about its mean position indefinitely, as indicated by curve (a) in figure 6.20. Real isolators however, even springs, have a certain degree of internal damping, the result of which is that energy is progressively removed from the system so that the amplitude of vibration steadily reduces, as shown in curve (b) of figure 6.20. If the amount of damping present is very large, the movement of the mass back to its rest position

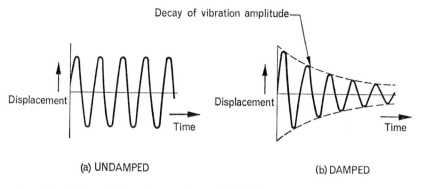

Fig. 6.20. Effect of damping on free vibration

after the initial deflection will be very sluggish, and it may not overshoot and oscillate at all. If the amount of damping is just sufficient for this to happen, i.e. just sufficient for the mass to return to its mean position in minimum time without overshoot, we say that the system has "critical" or "dead beat" damping. A measure of the amount of damping present in any isolating system, is the *damping ratio*, or the ratio of actual damping present, to that required for critical damping.

In addition to affecting the way the machine vibrates on its own, damping will also have a marked effect upon the transmissibility when the machine is running. The equation analogous to equation (6.8) when damping is present is:

$$\text{Transmissibility} = \sqrt{\frac{1 + 4D^2\left(\frac{f}{f_0}\right)^2}{\left(1-\left(\frac{f^2}{f_0}\right)\right)^2 + 4D^2\left(\frac{f}{f_0}\right)^2}} \qquad (6.9)$$

Where D is the damping ratio

f is the frequency of the driving force, Hz

f_0 is the *undamped* natural frequency of the system, Hz.

This equation is shown graphically in figure 6.18 for $D = 20$ per cent and $D = 100$ per cent. Two important effects of damping are clearly shown. First, the frequency ratio for maximum transmissibility is generally lower than for the equivalent undamped amount. Second, at high values of forcing frequency, transmissibility varies with the amount of damping present.

The foregoing principles are fundamental to the behaviour of vibration isolators. The more practical points like choice of materials, and installation, are described in Chapter 7.

CHAPTER 7

Noise control in practice

By following Chapters 4 and 5, we have calculated how much noise reduction we are going to need in any particular set of circumstances, and in Chapter 6 we learned of the basic principles we will have to employ in order to achieve it.

Now we need to know the practical means available. To do this we look at each of the situations described earlier and discuss the methods that have to be used in each case. First, some general comments.

Any noise control problem can be represented by the very simple energy flow diagram shown in figure 7.1. From this we see that we have one of two options.

1. Reduce the strength of the source.
2. Impede the acoustic energy along its transmission path.

In nearly all the cases we shall be considering in this chapter, the relevant method involves impeding the transmission path. In the majority of cases the source will be some piece of proprietary machinery or equipment. The engineer concerned with noise control rarely has any scope for influencing the amount of sound power actually produced by the machine, except perhaps indirectly by selecting a quieter model—if one is available! We shall not be generally concerned here, therefore, with the design of quiet machines, but rather with coping with the energy once it is produced. In other words, we shall assume that in all the cases to be considered, the situations represented by the formulae in Chapters 4 and 5, SWL is pre-determined.

Having said this, it should be mentioned that there are "classes" of non-proprietary sources which often cause trouble, and which the noise control

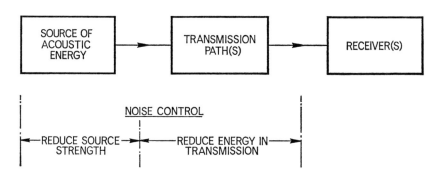

Fig. 7.1. Energy flow diagram

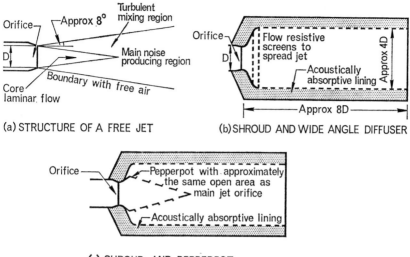

(a) STRUCTURE OF A FREE JET　　　　(b) SHROUD AND WIDE ANGLE DIFFUSER

(c) SHROUD AND PEPPERPOT

Fig. 7.2. Examples of jet noise mufflers

engineer can reduce in strength. Before going on to the more usual methods of control, therefore, we will examine how much can be achieved by these "source control" methods.

Noise control at source
Sources involving air or gas movement

Except for ventilating fans and blowers, which are discussed in more detail later, the most frequent offenders in this class are steam or process air exhausts and blow-offs, and control valves in pipe-lines.

(a) Pressure relief and dump systems

Exhausts of this type form free jets surrounded by air at rest, and produce noise in exactly the same way as aircraft jets. Figure 7.2a shows diagrammatically the structure of a jet. Between the boundary of the jet and the air at rest, there is a very high shear velocity gradient, the effect of which is to produce a mixing region of turbulent flow in which pressure fluctuations on individual elements of air are very intense, and act as individual noise sources. The frequency spectrum produced is very broad and has its maximum levels at frequencies determined by the efflux velocity and the size of the jet. A very approximate estimate of the order of sound power level to be expected from a free jet is given in figure 7.3.

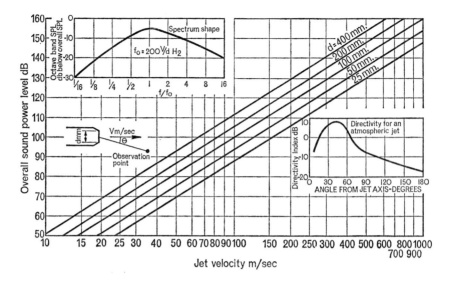

Fig. 7.3. Design chart for estimating jet and valve noise

EXAMPLE 7.1

Part of a new process plant is to incorporate an atmospheric dump for waste steam. The vent pipe is 150 mm in diameter, and when operating it will discharge at an exit velocity of approximately 225 m/sec vertically upwards. Estimate the sound pressure level in the octave bands from 63 Hz to 8000 Hz, that may be expected at an observation point which is 75 m from the jet discharge, and in a direction approximately 100° from the jet axis.

From fig. 7.3, the overall sound power level produced by a 150 mm pipe discharging at 225 m/sec is 124 dB.

From equation (4.5), the overall SPL at 75 m, and 100° is given by:

$$SPL = 124 - 20 \log (75) + DI (100°) - 11 \text{ dB}$$
$$= 76 + DI (100°) \text{ dB}$$

From the directivity chart in figure 7.3, DI (100°) = −10 dB
Then,   overall SPL = 66 dB.

To determine the shape of the octave band spectrum we first evaluate f_o, the frequency at which the spectrum peaks, i.e.,

$$f_o = \frac{200 \times 225}{150} = 300 \text{ Hz}$$

From Table 1.5, we find that 300 Hz falls in the octave band centred on 250 Hz. Thus the peak sound pressure will appear in this band. The others are determined as follows:

Octave Band Centre Freq	Hz	63	125	250	500	1000	2000	4000	8000
Overall SPL	dB	66	66	66	66	66	66	66	66
Spectrum correction (fig. 7.3)	dB	−16	−10	−5	−7	−12	−16	−20	−25
Octave Band SPL	dB	50	56	61	59	54	50	46	41

There are two ways of treating a sound of this nature. One is to reduce the jet velocity and the other is to provide local absorption around the source (which is normally about five to ten diameters downstream of the jet orifice), in the form of a lined shroud.

Steam jets in particular are amenable to one method of reducing efflux velocity which has been found successful—water injection. If cold water is mixed with high temperature steam just before the jet efflux, the steam condenses and its density increases. For a given mass flow (the additional mass of the water is usually small), this means a reduction in jet velocity, the effect of which can again be estimated approximately from figure 7.3.

Reduction of velocity with other jets is not so straightforward as it may appear. If it is achieved by simply stepping up the diameter of the pipe a short distance back from the efflux, all one does is generate another jet source at the step, the sound energy of which then travels to the end. Nevertheless, provided the stepping is carried out a very long distance from the efflux, some reduction can be achieved. First one gets a reduction from the lower velocity of the new atmospheric jet as indicated in figure 7.3.

The radiation from this is calculated using the new value of overall sound power level, following exactly the same procedure as illustrated in Example 7.1. We then have to consider the passage of energy from the new jet formed at the step in pipe diameter. The *total* power generated here can be estimated directly from figure 7.3. This power however does not radiate freely as does the power from a jet formed in full air. Instead, it travels along the new larger diameter pipe in much the same way as fan noise in a ventilating system. It might be thought that the losses from wall absorption, and reflection at bends would be the same as those described in Chapter 5, but unless the new pipe is similar in construction to a ventilating duct (i.e. sheet metal), it is safer to assume there are no losses between the step and the jet discharge. Here however there will be a loss due to reflection at the open end, which can be estimated directly from figure 5.7.

Once having emerged from the jet pipe the energy will propagate freely into the atmosphere, but the directivity of the radiation will be quite different from that of the atmospheric jet. Sound which is radiated from the end of a pipe after having travelled along it, will have a directivity pattern similar to that shown in figure 5.12. The values of directivity index obtained from figure 5.12 however must be reduced by 3 dB for the case of the open end of a pipe, since the baffle effect of the wall is not present. In other words, the 3 dB accounts for the difference between spherical propagation (open end of the pipe) and hemispherical propagation (louvre in a large wall).

EXAMPLE 7.2

It is proposed to reduce the noise from the steam jet described in Example 7.1 by expanding from the original 150 mm vent pipe to 300 mm giving a new efflux velocity of 56 m/sec—the expansion being some 10 m back from the discharge end. Estimate the new sound pressure level that might be expected at 75 m in a direction 100° to the jet axis.

(a) *Sound pressure level due to new 300 mm jet*

From figure 7.3 at 56 m/sec overall SWL = 94 dB.

This is a reduction of 30dB on the original SWL produced and since directivity is the same, we can write directly from the result of Example 7.1 that,

Overall SPL = 66 − 30

= 36 dB

The frequency at which peak sound pressure level occurs is given, as before, by

$$f_o = \frac{200 \times 56}{300} = 37 \text{ Hz (31·5 Hz octave band)}$$

The new octave band SPL is then given by:

Octave Band Centre Freq	Hz	63	125	250	500	1000	2000	4000	8000
Overall SPL	dB	36	36	36	36	36	36	36	36
Spectrum correction (fig. 7.3)	dB	−7	−12	−16	−20	−25	−30	−35	−40
Octave Band SPL	dB	29	24	20	16	11	6	1	−4

Compared with the previous situation (example 7.1) the new jet shows a dramatic improvement.

(b) *Sound pressure level due to jet formed at 150 mm/300 mm step*

Since the velocity of the jet and the jet pipe diameter are the same as in example 7.1 we have that the overall SWL is 124 dB. Because the loss due to reflection at the open end of the 300 mm pipe is frequency dependant, we have to express this overall SWL as octave band levels before we consider its progress from the jet. This is calculated as before using fig. 7.3 i.e.,

$$f_o = \frac{200 \times 225}{150} = 300 \text{ Hz}$$

The sound pressure level at the observation point is calculated as follows:

Octave Band Centre Freq	Hz	63	125	250	500	1000	2000	4000	8000
Overall SWL	dB	124	124	124	124	124	124	124	124
Spectrum correction (fig. 7.3)	Hz	−16	−10	−5	−7	−12	−16	−20	−25
Octave Band SWL	dB	108	114	119	117	112	108	104	99
Reflection at 300 mm dia. opening (fig. 5.7)	dB	−15	−10	−5	−2	0	0	0	0
(i) SWL radiated	dB	93	104	114	115	112	108	104	99
DI (0°) (fig. 5.11)	dB	+3	+4	+6	+6	+8	+9	+9	+9
(ii) DI (100°) (extrapolated from fig. 5.12—3 dB)	dB	0	−1	−4	−4	−13	−25	−25	−25
(iii) − (20 log (75) − 11)	dB	−48	−48	−48	−84	−48	−48	−48	−48
From equation (4.6) SPL = (i) + (ii) + (iii)	dB	45	55	62	63	51	35	31	26

If we compare this sound pressure level with that produced by the original jet (example 7.1) we find that significant improvement is gained only at 2000 Hz and above. While this helps, it hardly solves the problem, particularly since the level at 500 Hz has been increased. On the other hand, we notice that the noise at the observation point is determined entirely by the new source formed at the pipe expansion. Moreover, the energy is produced sufficiently far back along the pipe for us to be able to control it, before it reaches the end of the pipe. An ordinary packaged absorptive silencer of the type used in ventilating systems (these are described later in this chapter) will usually suffice, providing suitable protection against wet or corrosive gas is given to the absorbing material.

We therefore conclude that one way of controlling jet noise is to locate the high intensity source somewhere within the system, and reduce the energy before it is allowed to propagate from the atmospheric end.

In cases where it is essential to produce the high intensity jet in free air, we have then to resort to the use of some form of absorptive shroud.

Absorptive shrouds over free jets can be most effective. They perform two functions. One is to provide a shield against direct radiation from the source, and the other is to absorb the energy by multiple reflection inside the shroud—the diameter of the shroud outlet being designed to give a fixed jet velocity which is acceptable. If the shroud is made sufficiently long to prevent direct radiation at angles greater than about 10 degrees either side of the jet axis, and the velocity is slowed using a diffuser combined with a flow resistive device such as a layer of wide mesh gauze (fig. 7.2b), a reduction of as much as 20 dB in radiated sound power can be achieved. The low frequency attenuation is limited by the absorptive properties of the shroud lining material. As an alternative to thick lining, a cone of "pepper pot" construction is sometimes used (fig. 7.2c). The idea here is to break the single large jet into a number of small diameter jets. This does not have much effect on the total sound power produced, but it does cause a shift to the high frequency end of the spectrum where it is more easily absorbed by the lining.

The main problem with shrouds of this type is that they produce some degree of back pressure. While this may not be a problem if the gas is simply being dumped, it will probably be unacceptable for emergency blow-off or safety release systems. Fortunately the degree of the problem is reduced somewhat by the (hopefully) infrequent occurrence of the noise. Such devices have to be tested periodically of course, but a little public relations work beforehand on any residential area likely to be affected, could have as much effect as a muffler on the reduction of annoyance. If that does not work, about the only option open is to employ the ejector or corrugated nozzle technique used on aircraft engines where back pressure is critical. The principle here is to induce a secondary air flow around the primary jet, which, because its velocity is somewhere between that of the jet and that of the air at rest, acts as a sort of "lubricant" between the two and reduces the intensity of the noise-producing regions of turbulence. It must be emphasized though, that whilst mid frequency reductions of up to about 10 dB are possible, the design is still somewhat empirical, and will almost certainly require some degree of experimentation.

(b) *Control valves*

Practically all that has been said about the mechanism of generating noise in jets, applies to control valves. All that happens is that, as the orifice formed by the valve gets smaller, the velocity of gas increases, and we have a jet formed in the pipe just downstream of the valve. The form of the jet is modified somewhat by the pipe walls but the generating mechanism is basically the same. In fact, the sound power levels predicted by figure 7.3 have been found to be reasonably close to some observed cases.

The calculation of sound pressure level due to radiation of valve noise from the open end of a discharge pipe into which it may feed, is the same as described in part (b) of the solution to example 7.2. The sound power produced can be assumed to be that of a free jet of velocity equal to the maximum velocity through the valve port, and of diameter equal to the opening.

Valve noise generally becomes important when gas flows and valve settings are in the right combination to produce supersonic flow through the orifice. Again, as a general rule, pressure ratios across the valve less than about 1·75 do not normally present many problems. Where high pressures are inevitable, the aim should be to reduce them as progressively as possible rather than in one step. One way of course, is to drop the pressure through a number of valves in series, each having a pressure ratio not greater than the 1·75 mentioned earlier. An alternative method, which has been the subject of some research in recent years, is to incorporate in

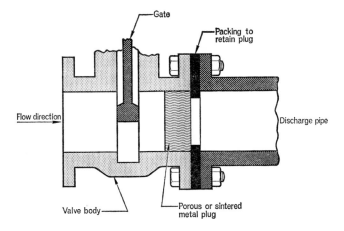

Fig. 7.4. Method of reducing valve noise

the pipe immediately after the valve gate, a plug of porous, or sintered metal through which all the gas must pass (fig. 7.4). The effect of this is to slow the high velocity jet progressively so that the region of high shear gradients characteristic of a single jet, do not have chance to develop. Reductions of 15 to 20 dB at all frequencies have been obtained on some large valves using this method.

One peculiarity of valve noise not encountered in the free jet, is "pipe-ringing". The combination of very high acoustic pressures in the mixing region of the jet, and possibly the direct impingement of the jet onto the pipe wall, can set the wall vibrating. In high pressure systems particularly, the wall will probably be very stiff and have a number of well defined resonances in the mid to high frequency range. Since the excitation forces (acoustic and hydrodynamic) have a broad frequency spectrum, the components at frequencies corresponding to the pipe resonant frequencies will pass through the wall relatively unimpeded. The result is that a very strong discrete frequency noise is radiated outside the pipe.

Although as we have seen when discussing transmission through walls (Chapter 6), that addition of damping to the pipe walls will theoretically cut down the amplitude of the resonant vibration, the usually high mass of the wall reduces the effect of damping by itself. It is more effective in such cases to add a mass lagging to the outside of the pipe as shown in figure 7.5. By choosing a sufficiently thick resilient layer, one can make the outer skin act in effect like a separate mass insulation. One rarely achieves a reduction equal to the sound reduction index of the second skin because

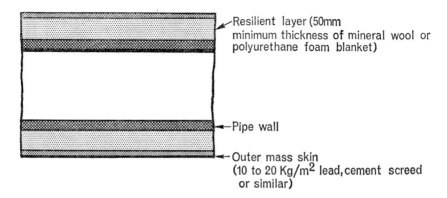

Resilient layer (50mm minimum thickness of mineral wool or polyurethane foam blanket)

Pipe wall

Outer mass skin (10 to 20 Kg/m^2 lead, cement screed or similar)

Fig. 7.5. Mass lagging to reduce pipe "ring"

there is always some degree of coupling, as we saw with double skin panels in the previous chapter, but the reductions that are achieved will normally be found sufficient to remove the discrete frequency components. Needless to say the lagging must be applied over the whole length of the pipe which is affected, including the valve body if necessary. This is fairly easy to determine by measuring the surface vibration of the pipe along its length using an accelerometer pick up.

One point often overlooked is that supports rigidly clamped to the pipe are very efficient carriers of vibration energy to nearby structure, which in turn may very efficiently transform the vibration received into airborne noise. If lagging the "source" pipe is to be effective therefore, it is essential to replace rigid with resilient supports along the treated length.

(c) Air exhausts from small actuators and hand tools

Worthy of special mention, are the small high pressure relief exhausts from the large variety of hand tools and air operated machine actuators almost universally encountered in all types of workshop. Because the size of the exhaust port is small, the characteristic frequencies produced by the jet itself, or its impingement upon some nearly solid structure, lie in the mid to high frequency range of the spectrum—say from 500 Hz upwards. The power produced at these frequencies is not normally sufficient to cause widespread nuisance, as in the case of the large mass flow exhausts referred to earlier, but they can be very annoying to operators in the vicinity, interfering with speech communication, and even constituting a hearing damage risk (see Chapter 2).

Again, because of the nature of the machines involved, it is seldom possible to incorporate absorptive devices of the type that were examined earlier. A very effective treatment however is simply to pipe the exhaust away. A small diameter, thick walled PVC or rubber tube will prevent the jet from fully developing its noise sources immediately after the exhaust port. If the tube is long enough, friction losses inside will slow the eventual discharge velocity from the end (obviously it must not present sufficient back pressure to impair the efficiency of the actuator). This will give some reduction, but the most important thing is that the source is now located away from the machine, probably in a place where absorptive treatment, if still required, can be more easily applied.

Impact noise

Many machines rely upon impulsive type loading for their operation— e.g. drop hammers, power presses, etc. From the point of view of the machine user, it is virtually impossible to reduce this noise at source by modifying the basic design of the machine. He has to rely upon full or partial enclosure of the type we shall be discussing later.

Having made that point, there remains a wide range of machines where impact noise is an incidental result of the main operation. Collection hoppers for solid material, or vibratory conveyors, are just two examples. The problem here is that the basic generating mechanism, the impulsive force of one solid body against a relatively large solid surface, is virtually flat in its frequency spectrum. The sharper the pulse and the shorter its duration, the higher is the frequency content as indicated in figure 7.6, and it is interesting to compare this frequency spectrum with the examples in figure 1.5.

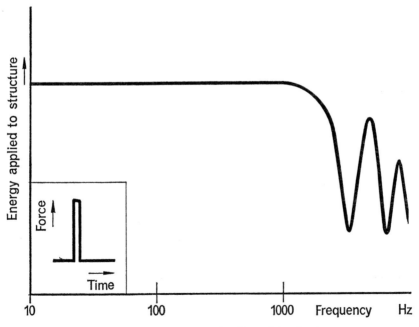

Fig. 7.6. Typical frequency spectrum of an impulsive load

Because the single impulse contains all frequencies, the surface it strikes will obviously vibrate at one or more of its resonant frequencies—a bell is an excellent example of how efficient this process can be at producing noise. With a single impulse, the noise is not sustained but dies away as the amplitude of vibration decays. If now we repeat the impulsive force many times per second, as would happen if a continuous stream of objects were falling on the surface, then the vibration—and of course the radiated noise—would be sustained continuously.

In fact, there are two effects of a continuous impulsive excitation of this type. One, as we have already seen, is a sustained discrete frequency note. This will happen if the surface of the hopper, conveyor or whatever is made of a very lightly damped material like steel or aluminium. Then a very effective treatment is to add damping to the material, either as an unconstrained layer of proprietary damping compound, or by replacing the sheet with one of the sandwich type materials now available which consists of two separate skins of the material required, separated by a layer of viscoelastic damping compound. A third choice, if the radiating surface is

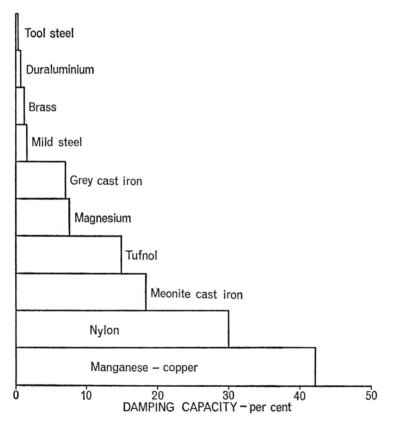

Fig. 7.7. Relative damping capacities of some common materials

more solid, such as a structural member, is to replace it with one of the proprietary high damping alloys on the market. These vary according to manufacturer, but all are based on a manganese copper alloy. Some idea of the damping capacity available, compared with more conventional materials is given in figure 7.7. All three treatments are capable of reducing *noise due to resonance* by as much as 15 dB. They have been mentioned in increasing order of cost.

The second effect of a continuous series of impulsive forces, is of course that non-resonant frequency vibrations are also sustained. In the case of the lighter damped material we have just discussed, they tend to be masked by the resonances. But where the material of the structure already has a high degree of damping, possibly as a result of treatment for resonance, strong broad frequency radiation can still result. The treatment for this depends upon the layout of the system. In the case where the impulsive forces are on the *inside* of a closed structure e.g. a cyclone collector or closed conveyor, and the noise is radiated from the *outside* surface, then a simple lagging treatment of the type described earlier in this chapter for pipes and control valves, will usually suffice—providing all the surfaces rigidly connected to the excited surface are also lagged, or separated by vibration isolators. Just how much needs to be lagged can often be determined by ear, or at least by vibration measurements on the appropriate surfaces.

When the hopper or conveyor is open so that both inside and outside surfaces are radiating, the solution of the problem usually resolves itself into the one of full or partial enclosure as discussed later. It may be possible however, depending upon the particular layout, to reduce the strength of the excitation and hence the radiated noise, by "cushioning" the impact. This can be achieved by the simple expedient of lining the hopper or conveyor with first a resilient material about 50 mm thick, and then a top skin of heavy duty rubber, nylon, or PVC sheet, which may be as thick as 6 mm, depending upon the engineering requirements of the installation (see fig. 7.8).

As a general comment on impact type sources, the requirement is to reduce as much as possible the amount of impulsive energy getting into the radiating surface. One way has just been mentioned. If treatment of this type is not possible, the question that should be asked is, can we reduce the energy of the object which is causing the impact? This might be achieved by breaking the fall with one, or even a number of inter-mediate barriers. It might be possible to provide a continuous guide that the object can slide along, rather than having to fall. This is particularly worth considering where the problem is noise from water splash.

When the energy getting into the radiating structure is fixed, the twin objectives must be to reduce the mechanical response of the structure, and to inhibit radiation from it. The examples quoted above demonstrate the approach that can be made.

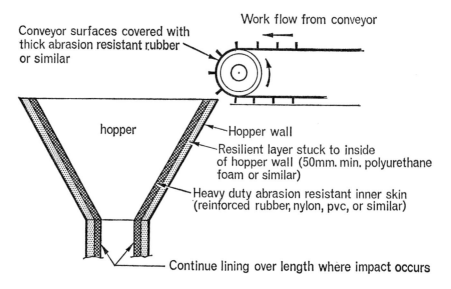

Conveyor surfaces covered with thick abrasion resistant rubber or similar

Work flow from conveyor

hopper

Hopper wall

Resilient layer stuck to inside of hopper wall (50mm. min. polyurethane foam or similar)

Heavy duty abrasion resistant inner skin (reinforced rubber, nylon, pvc, or similar)

Continue lining over length where impact **occurs**

Fig. 7.8. Example of treatment to reduce impact noise in conveyor systems

Noise control in transmission
Noise out of doors
(a) Normal atmospheric propagation

If we look at the equations governing the sound pressure level in the open air, equation (4.3) onwards, we see that, apart from reduction of the source sound power level, the only parameter we can control is the distance between source and receiver.

As a general rule therefore, the greater one can make this distance the better. Like all generalities, it needs qualification. Certainly there will always be a reduction in sound pressure level achieved by increasing distance from the source, but the law of diminishing returns was never so true. If we plot equation (4.4) graphically, as in figure 7.9 it is immediately obvious that to get a worthwhile reduction, greater than say 5 dB, we have to at least double the distance. This means that if we are at a small distance from the source, we can get a very worthwhile reduction by moving to a large distance. On the other hand, if we are already at a large distance, doubling it will probably be prohibitive.

Generally, gain of attenuation by alternative orientation of the source, thus taking advantage of a lower Directivity Index (equation (3.9)), is limited. Nevertheless, if Directivity Index is known to be less at certain angles to the source axis, it is worthwhile examining equation (4.8) to see if any significant reduction can be achieved. A good example here is the orientation of the atmospheric end of a ventilating duct (see fig. 5.12).

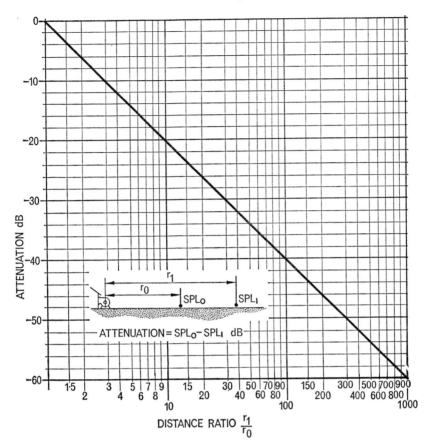

Fig. 7.9. Attenuation due to distance from source

Control of noise by variation of distance from source is really a matter for consideration in the planning stage. Rather, it is a matter of maximising distance from the receiver, as this is normally a fixed location, e.g. a residential area. The aim should be to locate the noisiest sources on the side of the site farthest from the most critical receiving point—taking care of course that this does not make some other sensitive area even more critical.

(b) Excess attenuation

Of the two types of excess attenuation we considered in Chapter 4, atmospheric effects and barriers, the former is of course virtually uncontrollable. The only way we can improve by design on the attenuation resulting from distance alone, is by placing a screen or a similar barrier between source and receiver.

The attenuation to be expected from a barrier of this type has already been given in figure 4.4. One very important point to realise is that with the order of magnitude of attenuation that can be expected, it is pointless to construct the barrier of heavy material to give a high transmission loss. As example 4.5 shows, the best that is usually achievable at low frequencies —around 125 Hz—is about 10 to 15 dB. A barrier construction with a sound reduction index greater than about 20 dB at this frequency would be needlessly expensive. Adequate barriers could therefore be constructed from corrugated asbestos-cement sheets, or cinder block, generally with a surface density of about 50 Kg/m². Recently, panels of high density rigid polyethylene have been tested as barriers to motorway noise with some success.

Again, the importance of considering at the planning stage the disposition of the source relative to sensitive areas cannot be over emphasised. Existing buildings are far cheaper barriers than ones that are specially constructed, and more effective, if they are large enough. Providing they extend far enough vertically and horizontally to give a good effective barrier "height", it is well worth attempting to locate a new sound source behind them. Figure 7.10 shows how the effective height can be estimated in some commonly encountered situations.

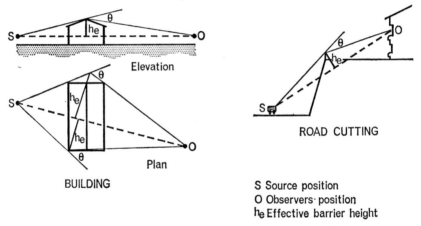

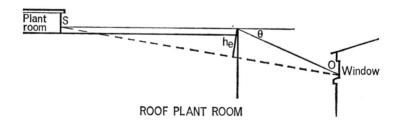

Fig. 7.10. Effective barrier height for some common situations

Noise in rooms

When we considered the behaviour of sound in a room, we found from equation 4.17 that the sound intensity, and therefore the sound pressure level, at any point, had two components—sound energy radiated directly from the source, and sound energy reaching the point after multiple reflection, the so-called reverberant sound energy.

Which component of the sound requires control depends upon their relative magnitudes at the observation point in question. If they are equal, for example, one can go to great lengths (and expense) to remove, say, the direct component almost entirely, but the nett reduction will only be 3 dB (see Table 1.2). Even if one component is very much higher than the other there is still no point in reducing it to less than about 6 dB below the other. This is illustrated in figure 7.11.

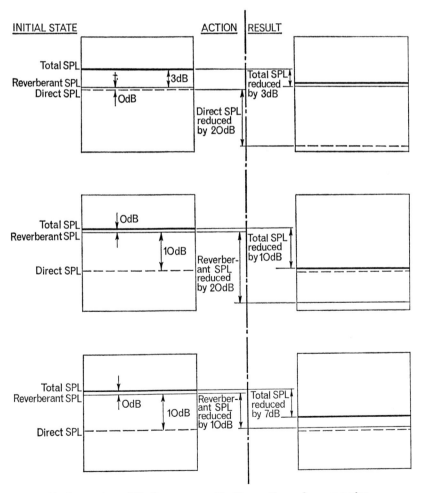

Fig. 7.11. Examples of limits on overall attenuation of room noise

(a) Control of the direct sound level

Let us first consider the case where the direct sound level is very much higher than the reverberant level, which by itself would be judged to be acceptable. In the previous discussion on controlling noise out of doors, we saw that basically we had two methods available. One was to increase distance, the other was to provide a screen.

Fundamentally, the same methods apply when the source and receiver are in the same enclosed space, but the scope is much more limited. Moving the source further away will undoubtedly reduce the direct sound pressure level—assuming that the increase of distance is worthwhile (fig. 7.9). In an enclosed space however, one is more likely to then be reducing the distance between the source and some other sensitive area in the room, in which case one has merely re-located the problem. Also in the process of trying to increase the original distance, it is quite possible that the source will end up near one of the walls or some other large reflecting surface. In that case any reduction due to increased distance will be offset by an increased directivity factor as shown in Table 4.1. The only solution then is to cover the reflecting surface with an absorptive treatment, giving an absorption coefficient of at least 0·7 at all frequencies of interest.

Barriers or screens can be just as effective in rooms as they are out of doors, but again they have to be positioned with some care. As far as the direct path between source and receiver is concerned, reductions of the order shown in figure 4.4 can be achieved. On the source side however, the barrier acts as a reflecting surface, and increases the Directivity Index for receiving points on that side. For this reason barriers used in enclosed spaces should always be covered with an absorptive blanket on the source side. In open plan offices, where the problem is always control of direct sound, acoustic screens provided with absorption on both sides are widely used. They can be obtained ready made in a variety of decorative finishes.

Where distance or screens do not provide sufficient attenuation one must resort to full or partial enclosure of the source, as described later in this chapter.

(b) Control of the reverberant sound

Referring once again to equation (4.17) we see that the one parameter controlling reverberant sound is the room constant R_c, or more precisely, since the room size is normally fixed, the average absorptive coefficient $\bar{\alpha}$.

The change in reverberant sound pressure level which occurs as a result of changing the average absorption coefficient, is given quite simply by

$$\text{SPL}_1 - \text{SPL}_2 = 10 \log \frac{\bar{\alpha}_2}{\bar{\alpha}_1} \text{ dB} \qquad (7.1)$$

Where SPL_1 and $\bar{\alpha}_1$ are respectively the initial sound pressure level and average absorptive coefficient.

SPL_2 and $\bar{\alpha}_2$ are respectively the sound pressure level and average absorptive coefficient after the room treatment.

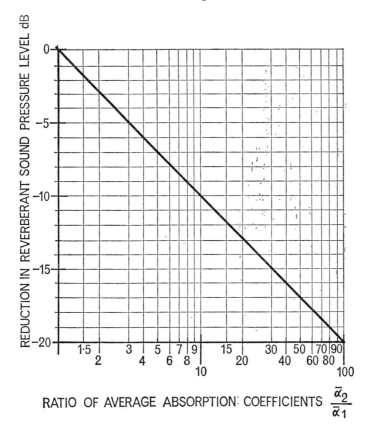

Fig. 7.12. Reduction in reverberant sound pressure level due to increased average absorption coefficient

Once again we find the law of diminishing returns. Equation (7.1) is shown graphically in figure 7.12 and it is clear that we will start to achieve worthwhile reductions in reverberant sound pressure level only if we can increase the average absorption coefficient by a factor of say 5 or more. If we have a very "hard" room like a plant room, or some other auxiliary room having highly reflective walls and no soft furnishings, this is not too difficult. The average absorptive coefficient may be as low as 0·05. All we have to do then, is line all the available surfaces with a highly absorptive treatment, to raise the average absorption coefficient to 0·25. At high frequencies we will probably do better than this, but at low frequencies say up to 500 Hz it is about the best that can be achieved in practice. The reason is of course that there will be areas like windows, doors possibly, and the floor, which cannot be treated.

The effect of leaving some areas untreated can be calculated from equation (4.12), as illustrated in example 4.6.

If it is considered that a worthwhile reduction can be achieved, it is still necessary to exercise some care in applying the treatment. First the choice. For mid to high frequency absorption, a porous type material will be required (see Chapter 5). Typical values of absorption coefficient will be found in Appendix A. For low frequency absorption it will be necessary to include some area of panel type absorption. Again some examples are given in Appendix A.

When the area and type of treatment has been determined from equation (4.12) and appendix A, the next thing to decide upon is the disposition of the various materials. As a general rule, this should be as even as possible. If for example, all the absorption is provided on the ceiling or on one wall, with other areas left untreated, it is possible to set up resonances between opposite parallel untreated surfaces. The result of this is that in some positions in the room, the sound will be unpleasantly loud compared to others.

Factories and workshops are particularly difficult to provide with absorptive treatment, especially where they rely upon large areas of the roof for light. Then the only way of providing sufficiently large absorption areas is to arrange deep vertical baffles below the lights as shown in figure 7.13.

All the foregoing comments have applied to the instance where the room was initially "hard" and absorptive treatment was justified. If we already have a room, such as an office or a residential apartment, the average absorptive coefficient will probably be about 0·2, due to the furnishings already there. In such cases it is virtually impossible to achieve anything but a marginal reduction simply by the general addition of absorptive treatment. One has to resort again to enclosure of the machine, as described later.

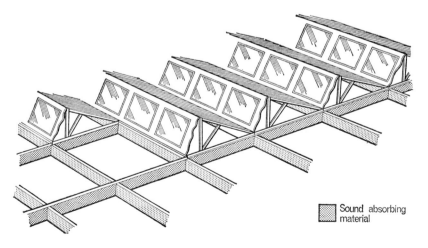

Sound absorbing material

Fig. 7.13. Method of increasing absorption in industrial buildings

Noise control between rooms

If we refer back to equation (4.18), which governed the reverberant sound pressure level in the receiving room due to a source located in an adjacent room, we find that we have four parameters determining the eventual sound pressure level. Not all are directly controllable. The area of the partition, for example, is probably fixed in advance by the requirements of the building. The total absorption in the receiving room is controllable to an extent, but as we have seen in the foregoing discussion, it is not always possible to achieve a worthwhile reduction in this way. This leaves us with two variables directly under our control.

(a) Source side sound pressure level

The first is the sound pressure level SPL_1, on the source side of the partition. If this is a reverberant sound pressure level, we can reduce it by absorptive treatment in the source room, as described earlier, or by enclosure as described later. Two important points should be emphasised. The first is that in the case of a machine that is located near the dividing partition, the level on the source side will obviously be a direct sound pressure level. One can reduce it to the reverberant level in the source room simply by locating the machine on the other side of the source room. This clearly does not apply if the problem is airborne sound transmission through a floor into the room below, but the second important point does. It is essential that the machine is mechanically isolated from the floor or the dividing wall. If it is not, the level in the receiving room may well be the result of structural vibration, and no amount of reduction of sound pressure level in the source room, will reduce the level in the receiving room (see fig. 7.14a). Vibration isolation is discussed in more detail later in this chapter.

(b) Sound reduction index

The second variable we have control over is the sound reduction index of the dividing partition. The principles governing sound reduction index have been discussed in some detail in Chapter 6. The combination of equation (4.18) to determine the sound reduction index required, and Appendix B, giving the value for various structures will enable a suitable structure to be selected in the design stage. Often however the problem will already have occurred with an existing structure, in which case we need to know either:

    (i) Why a given partition is not providing the attenuation expected of it;
    (ii) In the case of the source sound pressure level having been changed, how the sound reduction index can be increased.

(i) Control of indirect transmission

In the first case, the problem is most likely to be indirect transmission. One type has already been mentioned—inadequate vibration isolation (fig. 7.14a). The expected sound reduction index of a wall is based on the

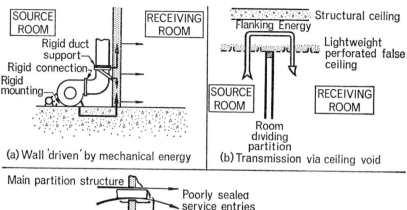

(a) Wall 'driven' by mechanical energy

(b) Transmission via ceiling void

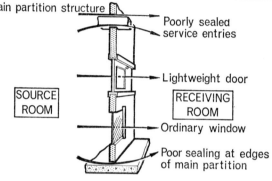

(c) Transmission through 'weak' areas

Fig. 7.14. Some commonly encountered reasons for loss of insulation

assumption that the wall is "forced" by acoustic pressures. If it is mechanically excited, there will appear to be a lower value.

Another type of flanking transmission commonly encountered, particularly in office buildings, is that which occurs over the top of modular partitions built up to the underside of suspended ceilings. Figure 7.14b shows diagrammatically the path that the sound energy takes. The reason that this happens is of course that the ceiling is provided only for *absorption*, and not for *insulation*. The perforations in the suspended tiles or metal trays allow very easy access for the acoustic energy to the absorptive blanket behind. Since this is usually a lightweight material, the energy passes through to the void, travels along past the top of the partition and down into the next room. The remedy, if a higher overall sound reduction index is required, is to continue the partition up to the underside of the structural slab.

Many walls between rooms, are not of course uniform in their structure throughout. Doors, windows, access holes for services, all constitute potentially "weak" areas in the wall, as indicated in figure 7.14c. Access holes for services are not much of a problem once the service is installed, the remedy being to caulk all round the edges of the hole with a good thickness of bitumastic sealing compound. If the hole is much oversize the gaps should first be plugged with blanket material such as mineral wool, wedged in firmly, as indicated in figure 7.23.

Doors and windows should be constructed to provide sufficient sound reduction index, taking into account their relative areas, to ensure that

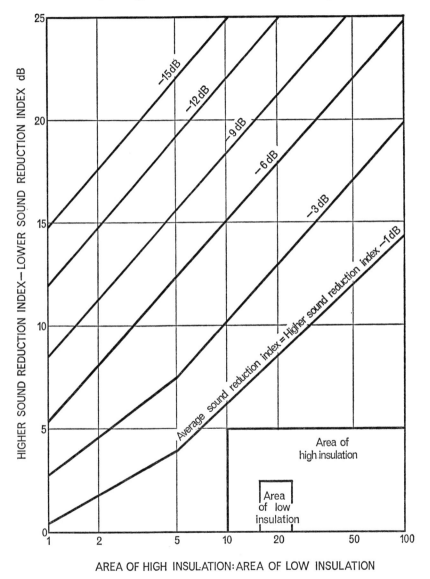

Fig. 7.15. Loss of sound insulation due to "weak" areas

the average sound reduction index of the complete partition (equation (4.19)) is not more than one or two decibels, below that of the main structure. The individual sound reduction indices required can be calculated from equation (4.20), or obtained graphically from fig. 7.15 which shows the loss of insulation to be expected if a wall contains an area of lower sound reduction index than that of the main structure.

If high insulation is required, windows will almost certainly have to be double glazed. For best results the following points should be noted.

1. The airspace between the two panes should be as large as possible, and in any case not less than 150 mm.
2. The panes should be mounted in separate frames on either side of the wall, and be held in rubber or neoprene moulding.
3. The panes should be of different thickness to minimise coupled resonances.
4. The reveals should be lined with acoustic tile, mineral wool, or similar absorptive material, to inhibit resonances of the cavity.

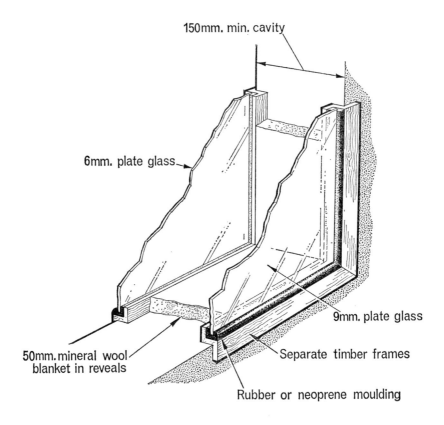

Fig. 7.16. Example of double glazed window construction

A typical construction is shown in figure 7.16, and representative values of sound reduction index for various constructions will be found in Appendix B.

As a general comment, it can be said that a door is only as good acoustically as its seal. However much care has been taken to select the correct construction, any gaps around the edges can practically nullify the potential.

The essential requirements are:

1. A positive airtight seal must be provided in a rebated frame all round the door, including the threshold.

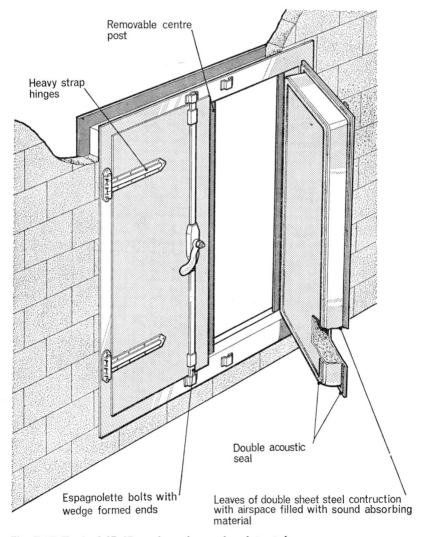

Removable centre post

Heavy strap hinges

Espagnolette bolts with wedge formed ends

Double acoustic seal

Leaves of double sheet steel contruction with airspace filled with sound absorbing material

Fig. 7.17. Typical 45 dB packaged sound resistant door

2. The door furniture (espagnolette bolts, or mortice handles) must be wedge formed so that fastening the door pulls it into the frame and compresses the seal.

3. The frame must be dead flat when fixed, so that the seal is compressed evenly all round.

Doors which require sound reduction indices greater than 25 dB, are best bought as a packaged unit. There are several proprietary doors on the market, offering average sound reduction indices up to 45 dB—equivalent to a 112 mm brick wall. They are supplied already fixed in a frame together with suitable furniture and seals. A typical "45 dB door" is shown in figure 7.17.

A problem which frequently occurs is the need for a fresh-air louvre in the outside wall of a mechanical services plant room, or even in the wall between two rooms. Any treatment to increase the sound reduction index of the hole, must of course allow the free passage of air. One way is to place on one, or both sides of the hole, a packaged silencer of the type used in ventilating systems. These are described in more detail later. More recently, the "acoustic louvre" has gained popularity. Aerodynamically, it acts much the same as an ordinary louvre, but instead of the normal

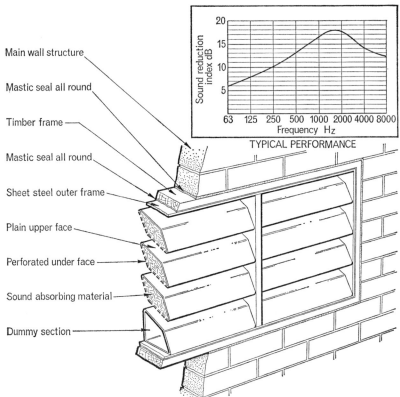

Main wall structure

Mastic seal all round

Timber frame

Mastic seal all round

Sheet steel outer frame

Plain upper face

Perforated under face

Sound absorbing material

Dummy section

TYPICAL PERFORMANCE

Fig. 7.18. Basic elements of an acoustic louvre

flat sheet vanes, those on the acoustic louvre are hollow, up to about 50 mm thick, with the underside (the side facing the noise source) formed from perforated sheet, and the intervening cavity filled with sound absorptive material. A typical construction is shown in figure 7.18, together with the value of sound reduction index that is achievable.

(ii) *Increasing the sound reduction index*

All the foregoing has been concerned with how to ensure that a wall provides the sound reduction index of which it is potentially capable. We turn now to the second problem often encountered, that where some change has increased the sound pressure level on the source side, and we have to increase the sound reduction index of an existing wall.

We saw in Chapter 6 that increasing insulation by the simple expedient of adding mass was another of the ubiquitous examples of the law of diminishing returns that occur in acoustics. We saw in fact that the first step forward, as it were, was to turn our single leaf partition into a double leaf construction. We may however need to go beyond this.

As in the case of the single leaf partition, increasing the overall sound reduction index by increasing the mass of the individual panels brings diminishing returns. There comes a point when the two panels arranged with a small (up to 100 mm) airspace gives very little improvement over a single wall of mass equal to twice the mass of one panel. As a rough guide if one requires more than 40 dB (average over the frequency range 100 Hz to 3200 Hz) from a light-weight partition, or 50 dB from a masonry partition, and airspaces well in excess of 100 mm are not acceptable, one has to start thinking of improving the mechanical isolation between the two panels.

With the "board and studding" type of construction this is not too difficult. One simply supports the panels on resilient spring clips fixed to the studding. An alternative is to stagger or slit the studding and/or stick the panels onto sheets of rigid glass fibre, or similar material, which in turn are fixed to the studding. An example of the improvement that can be achieved in this way is shown in figure 7.19. Note here however that this treatment must be carried out over the whole area of the partition. It is pointless to leave holes in the second skin for such items as switches, pipe brackets, conduit boxes and the like. These items must be removed, and re-fixed to the outside of the second skin (taking great care to ensure that in re-fixing them, the isolation of the second skin is not "bridged" by the fixing). Moreover, it is essential to seal the edges of the second skin to side walls, floor and ceiling of the room, by caulking with a mastic compound—again avoiding any solid bridging.

With masonry panels it is rather more difficult to achieve isolation, but one can get a 5 to 10 dB improvement by such treatment as replacing the normal strip wall ties with expanded metal, or similarly flexible ties, ensuring that the cavity is kept completely free from rubble during construction, and building each leaf on a neoprene pad.

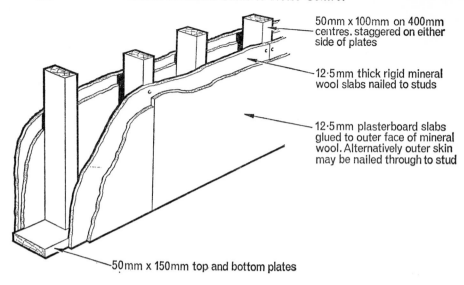

50mm x 100mm on 400mm centres. staggered on either side of plates

12·5mm thick rigid mineral wool slabs nailed to studs

12·5mm plasterboard slabs glued to outer face of mineral wool. Alternatively outer skin may be nailed through to stud

50mm x 150mm top and bottom plates

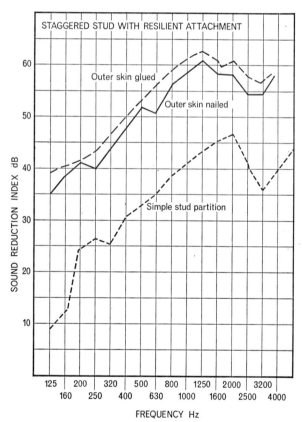

Fig. 7.19. Improvement of sound reduction index with resilient mounting

Again, the improvement to be gained by mechanical isolation is limited both with lightweight and masonry partitions. Generally one can get to something like 50 dB for lightweight partitions and 55 to 60 dB for masonry partitions, by these methods. Beyond this the performance is determined almost entirely by the amount of flanking energy which gets through footings and common edge supports.

If very high insulation is required, one has to look to methods of completely isolating rooms from each other. An example of the type of construction required to give an average sound reduction index in excess of 60 dB, is shown in fig. 7.20. Here one starts with a concrete slab floor which "floats" on a resilient blanket supported on the main structural floor. (Floating floor constructions are discussed later.) The inner walls of the room are built up on this slab inside the structural walls of the

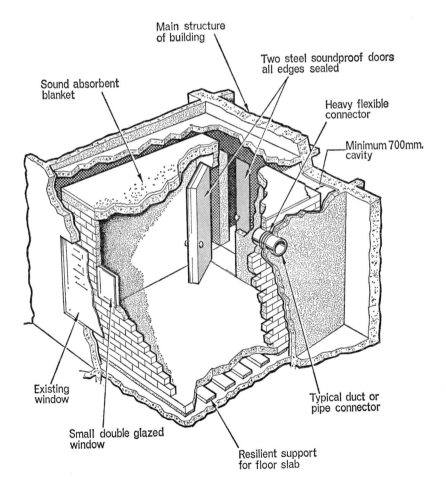

Fig. 7.20. Example of structure for very high insulation

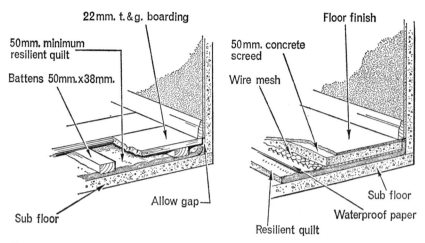

22mm. t. &g. boarding

50mm. minimum
resilient quilt

Battens 50mm.x38mm.

Floor finish

50mm. concrete
screed

Wire mesh

Allow gap

Sub floor

Sub floor

Waterproof paper

Resilient quilt

Fig. 7.21. Typical example of "floating floor" application

building, and the room is completed by casting a separate slab supported only by the inner walls.

Doors and windows must be constructed for high sound reduction index, as described previously. Any service entries must contain a heavy but flexible section to bridge the gap between the two rooms.

Floors

The treatment of floors for both high insulation against airborne noise, and low transmission of impact noises like footsteps, is worthy of special mention. The most usual treatment is to construct a "floating" floor on top of the main structural floor. Typical constructions for wood and concrete floors which give good impact and airborne sound insulation, are shown in figure 7.21. Again it is essential to make sure that no solid bridging path exists at the edges.

As in all the other cases discussed, we shall almost certainly be faced with the problem of improving the sound reduction index of, say, a plant room floor, where it is quite impossible to lay a floating floor in the plant room itself. The only recourse we have then is to suspend a *mass* ceiling on the underside of the plant room floor as indicated in figure 7.22. Note here the importance of mass in the suspended ceiling. The common practice of fixing sound absorbing ceiling tiles in the room underneath the plant room, will add absolutely nothing to the sound reduction index between the rooms. Mass is essential, and for maximum effect we have to invoke again the principle of separating the two leaves (plant room floor and added mass ceiling) as efficiently as possible by using resilient hangers. If required, to control reverberant noise in the room underneath, ceiling tiles can be fixed to the underside of the mass ceiling. If a suspended ceiling is required in the room below, this should be hung below the mass

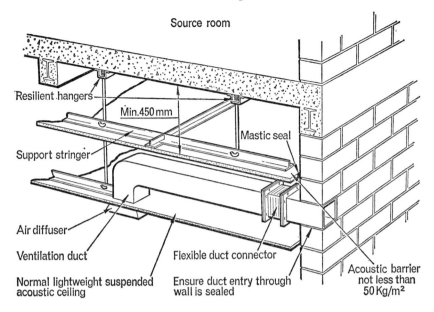

Source room

Resilient hangers

Min. 450 mm

Support stringer

Mastic seal

Air diffuser

Ventilation duct

Flexible duct connector

Normal lightweight suspended acoustic ceiling

Ensure duct entry through wall is sealed

Acoustic barrier not less than 50 Kg/m²

Fig. 7.22. Example of suspended ceiling construction to improve airborne sound insulation

ceiling, and carried on the same resilient supports, as should any recessed light fittings. Ventilation ducting in the normal suspended ceiling should also be "sprung", and a flexible vibration break incorporated in the duct just before it enters the vertical wall.

Practical design of enclosures

If we refer back to equation (4.28) which showed how much reduction we could expect by completely enclosing the source, we see that again we have two variables under our control—the absorption inside the enclosure, and the sound reduction index of the enclosure walls. (The radiating area, S_E, is more or less fixed by the physical size of the source to be enclosed). As far as attaining the required value of absorption and sound reduction index is concerned, previous statements in respect of treatment to rooms, and requirements for partitions will apply. All that needs to be added as a general point, is that with enclosures in particular, it is absolutely essential to provide as much absorption as possible inside. Neglect will result in a build up of reverberant sound inside the enclosure which in effect increases the sound power level to be contained.

Another vital requirement is complete mechanical isolation between source and enclosure. Preferably the machine itself should be vibration isolated from the floor and all its services, as described later in the section on vibration isolation. The enclosure can then rest directly on the floor without the risk of its structure being mechanically "driven". If there is any doubt, it is best to lay a pad of thick neoprene, or felt under the edges of the enclosure. Needless to say, all pipes, ducts and conduits which have to pass through the enclosure wall, must have vibration breaks in the form of flexible connectors, situated between the enclosure wall and the machine. Where high pressure precludes the use of a flexible pipe section, the hole in the enclosure wall should be a clearance hole, packed with felt or mineral wool, and caulked with a mastic sealant (see fig. 7.23).

Following these principles it should be a fairly straightforward matter to construct an enclosure, remembering the three design rules.

1. Walls must provide sufficient sound reduction index (allowing for the effect of weak areas like viewing ports and access panels).
2. Maximum absorption at all frequencies of interest must be provided *inside* the enclosure.
3. Mechanical isolation between enclosure structure, and the machine and its associated services, must be as complete as possible.

The more complicated the machine, generally speaking, the harder it will be found to put these principles into practice. The engineer faced with the prospect of having to provide an enclosure would be well advised to seek advice from one or other of the specialist companies who provide them in the form of pre-fabricated modular units. Adequate sound reduction index and internal absorption are taken care of by the basic construction of the enclosure panels, and moreover various types of panels are available to provide inspection windows, access doors, specially attenuated ventilation packs, and work inflow and outflow tunnels.

It is also possible to obtain proprietary units which are tailored to fit around one part of a machine where a particular noise source may be

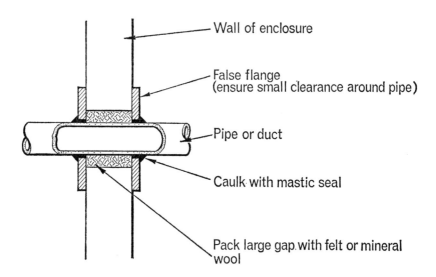

Fig. 7.23. Entry of high pressure service through sound insulating wall

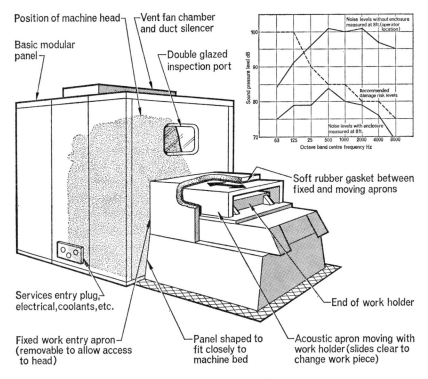

Position of machine head
Basic modular panel
Vent fan chamber and duct silencer
Double glazed inspection port
Soft rubber gasket between fixed and moving aprons
Services entry plug, electrical, coolants, etc.
End of work holder
Fixed work entry apron (removable to allow access to head)
Panel shaped to fit closely to machine bed
Acoustic apron moving with work holder (slides clear to change work piece)

Fig. 7.24. Example of special machine tool enclosure

located. This can be just as effective as enclosing the whole machine, *provided* that the enclosure also covers other parts of the machine that may be radiating, as a result of excitation by mechanical energy from the main source. A good example of this type of construction is shown in figure 7.24. Here the problem was a rotary swaging machine, in which the work, in the form of a bar, is clamped firmly in a vice and moved forward so that the end is inserted into the rotary swaging die. The main source was located in the tool head, but because the whole assembly had to be rigidly clamped, the energy from the impact loads on the bar, was travelling along it, and being radiated as noise from the vice and its carriage. The enclosure therefore had to contain the noise from the main source and the work holder, but at the same time allow work to be fixed into, and removed from the vice. Shaping the main enclosure to fit the bed of the machine, contained the noise from the head, and an "apron" covering the work piece and moving with it, contained the secondary radiation. The reduction achieved is also shown in figure 7.24.

Even a purpose-designed enclosure would be restrictive for some machines of course, and then one has to look to partial enclosure. An extreme example of a partial enclosure is a simple barrier of the type discussed earlier. From this we could go to a two-sided enclosure, add a

FIGURES REFER TO AVERAGE CHANGE IN SPL IN THE FREQUENCY RANGE 500Hz to 4000Hz

ENCLOSURE WITH ONE SIDE OPEN

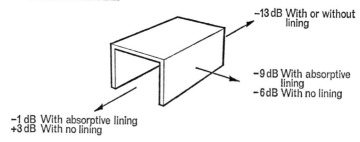

−13 dB With or without
       lining

−9 dB With absorptive
       lining
−6 dB With no lining

−1 dB With absorptive lining
+3 dB With no lining

OPEN SIDED ENCLOSURE AND MOVEABLE SCREEN

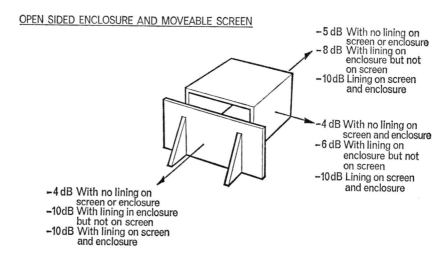

−5 dB With no lining on
        screen or enclosure
−8 dB With lining on
        enclosure but not
        on screen
−10dB Lining on screen
        and enclosure

−4 dB With no lining on
        screen and enclosure
−6 dB With lining on
        enclosure but not
        on screen
−10dB Lining on screen
        and enclosure

−4 dB With no lining on
        screen or enclosure
−10dB With lining in enclosure
        but not on screen
−10dB With lining on screen
        and enclosure

TUNNEL

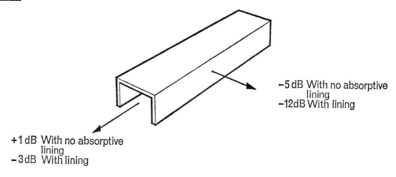

−5 dB With no absorptive
        lining
−12dB With lining

+1 dB With no absorptive
        lining
−3 dB With lining

Fig. 7.25. The effect on direct sound pressure level of some partial enclosures

roof, and so on, up to the complete enclosure. Some examples are shown in figure 7.25, with the order of sound reduction that might be expected. Note again the importance of providing absorption inside, and of avoiding any sort of rigid mechanical coupling with the machine.

Ventilation of enclosures should not be overlooked. Many processes, electric motors, blowers etc. require an adequate air supply, either to prevent overheating or to enable them to function efficiently, which must be provided via an attenuated ventilation unit.

Control of design in ventilating systems
Reduction of fan noise

Following the procedures described in Chapter 5 we will have calculated, for a given system, the room sound pressure levels due to the passage of sound energy from the fan, along the duct system, and into the room. Comparing the sound pressure level with the criterion for the room, gives the attenuation that is required. The mechanical services engineer has basically two ways of achieving this:

(*a*) Fan selection.

(*b*) Added attenuation in the system.

(*a*) *Fan Selection*

The system designer may well be forgiven for thinking that he has no more control over the source sound power level in a ventilating system, than he has over that of any other item of equipment he specifies. To an extent this is true. The basic sound power output of a given fan is very much the responsibility of the fan designer, and there is nothing that the system designer can do to reduce it, once it is in his system. He has, however, some measure of control, in that by careful selection, he can ensure that he has the fan giving lowest sound output for a given duty. What factors then must he consider?

One of the most important is the type of fan, or more precisely, the detailed frequency characteristics of the noise that will be produced by different types. As we shall see when discussing later the characteristics of silencers for ventilating systems, the most difficult noise to attenuate is low frequency noise. The system itself will provide some low frequency attenuation of course, as we saw in Chapter 5, but it is a rare system that does not require some additional low frequency attenuation, particularly in schemes for hospitals, schools, concert halls, etc. It is also a matter of practical experience that the amount, and hence cost, of additional absorptive treatment required, is almost without exception governed by the attenuation required in the 125 Hz and 250 Hz frequency bands, with the 63 Hz band occasionally being the critical one. The lesson is obvious— where noise is critical, the type of fan selected should be the one producing the lowest sound power levels at low frequencies.

It is also very important that wherever possible, the comparison are made on the basis of actual test results, rather than on predictions like the empirical formulae in equation (5.1). While these formulae have their uses in the preliminary design stage, they cannot be relied upon for an accuracy better than ± 5 dB, and the error may be as high as 10 dB in individual frequency bands.

Now the effect of duty. Having decided upon the type of fan, the system designer should look at the selection to see if he is operating the fan at its most efficient duty point. The noise from most fans is sensitive to some degree or other, to change of duty. Figure 7.26 shows the effect of change of duty on the noise produced. The occurrence of minimum noise level in the region of maximum aerodynamic efficiency is quite characteristic of fan noise. Operation at lower static pressures is not so hazardous as far as noise is concerned—although centrifugal fans tend to produce rather higher levels relative to the minimum level, at free air conditions than do axial fans. On the other hand, trying to squeeze too much performance out of the fan, and operating at static pressures well in excess of the design point, can have a very serious effect on noise, certainly 5 dB and often up to 10 dB. In the first place then, the size and speed of the fan should be selected so that when installed it operates as near as possible to its maximum efficiency point. In addition the system designer should fix maximum and minimum duties likely to be encountered on either side of the estimated design duty, and obtain from the fan manufacturer the likely change in noise levels over that range.

There is one other thing the system designer can do about the sound power level of the fan. By unsuitable installation design, he can cause the fan to produce noise *considerably in excess* of its potential minimum. If the flow into the fan impeller is non-uniform or is highly turbulent, the individual blades on the impeller are subjected to randomly occurring

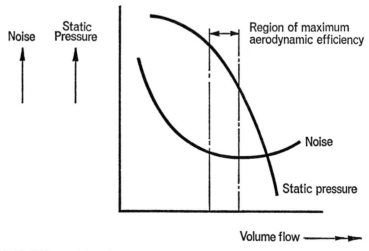

Fig. 7.26. Effect of fan duty on noise

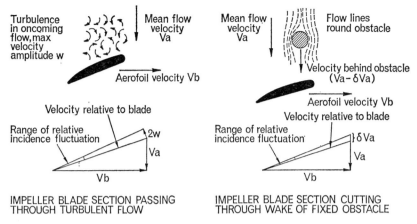

IMPELLER BLADE SECTION PASSING
THROUGH TURBULENT FLOW

IMPELLER BLADE SECTION CUTTING
THROUGH WAKE OF FIXED OBSTACLE

Fig. 7.27. Mechanism of generating additional noise from fan

pressure fluctuations, in addition to the steady aerodynamic forces upon them. As we saw when discussing secondary noise in Chapter 5, the combination of a fluctuating pressure (the turbulent flow) and a rigid surface (the impeller blade) acts very well as a source of acoustic energy. Figure 7.27 shows two mechanisms by which fluctuating pressures can arise on a fan impeller blade due to variations in the relative angle of incidence of the airflow onto it. The important point is that this mechanism of generating noise is *additional* to the basic noise generation of the blade itself. In practical terms, one could be faced with as much as 10 dB more than the fan would normally produce in a smooth uniform flow. Figure 7.28 shows some typical cases to be avoided. Although examples are cited for axials, similar considerations apply to all types of fan. Obviously there will always be cases when turbulence generating elements have to be located upstream of the fan. As a general rule, the aim should be to allow a distance of at least one impeller diameter between an upstream obstruction, and the fan, as a "settling" length for rough flow.

(b) Added attenuation in the system

One way of attenuating noise during its passage along a duct, fixing absorptive lining to the sides, has been discussed in Chapter 6. This is a perfectly acceptable way of controlling noise, and is frequently used. One simply decides upon the length of duct that will require treatment using for example figure 6.13. Note however that for reasonable low frequency performance, it is necessary to use thick lining material, and a minimum of 100 mm is recommended. Where only a short length of lined duct is required, to cope with mid frequency noise, it is possible to obtain a proprietary unit which simply replaces a length of the plain duct. Typical performances for proprietary attenuators consisting of a lined circular duct of length 1·5 times the internal diameter, are shown in Table 7.1.

For almost any significant low frequency performance, it will be necessary to employ the principle of "splitting" the duct into sections whose width is very much smaller than their height. In fact it may be necessary to reduce the width of the airway to as little as 50 or 75 mm. The performance of narrow lined airways of this type is shown for the particular case of a 100 mm lining on either side of the airway in figure 7.29.

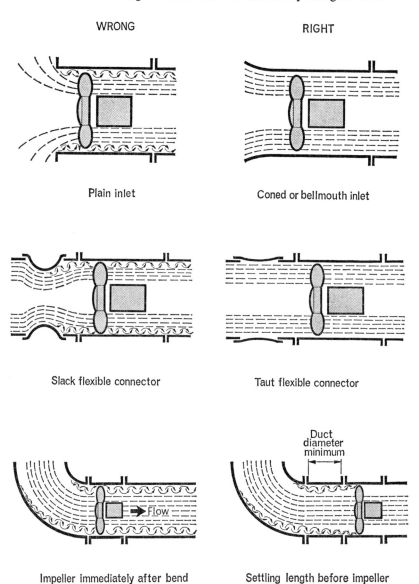

WRONG

RIGHT

Plain inlet

Coned or bellmouth inlet

Slack flexible connector

Taut flexible connector

Impeller immediately after bend

Settling length before impeller

Fig. 7.28. Examples of noise generating installations

TABLE 7.1

Performance of packaged cylindrical fan silencers

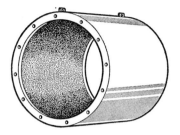 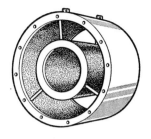

Silencer internal diam. D mm	Octave band mid-frequencies							
	63 Hz	125 Hz	250 Hz	500 Hz	1000 Hz	2000 Hz	4000 Hz	8000 Hz
	dB	dB	dB	dB	dB	dB	dB	dB
300	0	0	2	5	10	12	10	7
380	0	1	3	6	11	11	9	6
480	0	1	4	8	12	11	8	5
600	0	2	5	10	12	10	7	5
760	1	3	6	11	11	9	6	3
960	1	4	8	12	11	8	5	2
1220	2	5	10	12	10	7	4	2
1520	3	6	11	11	9	6	3	2

Silencer internal diam. D mm	Octave band mid-frequencies							
	63 Hz	125 Hz	250 Hz	500 Hz	1000 Hz	2000 Hz	4000 Hz	8000 Hz
	dB	dB	dB	dB	dB	dB	dB	dB
300	3	4	4	10	17	23	25	18
380	4	3	6	12	19	25	22	16
480	5	3	8	15	21	26	20	15
600	4	4	10	17	23	25	18	14
760	3	6	12	19	25	22	16	12
960	3	8	15	21	26	20	15	10
1220	4	10	17	23	25	18	14	9
1520	6	12	19	25	22	16	12	8

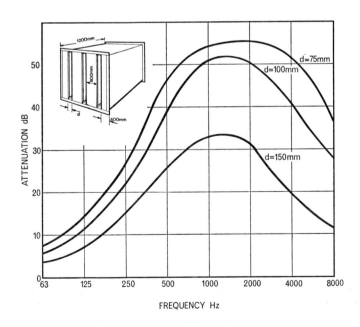

Fig. 7.29. Typical attenuation from 1200mm packaged "splitter" silencer

Again, packaged "splitter" silencers can be obtained ready made in a variety of overall dimensions to suit the physical space available, and the limiting additional pressure loss available from the fan. The general rule is that airway and length determine the attenuation, while width and height determine pressure loss, i.e.:

For higher attenuation—Reduce airway.

Increase length.

For lower resistance —Increase height.

Increase width (i.e. increase the number of airway/splitter modules).

It will often be found necessary to make the width and height of a splitter silencer greater than that of the parent duct, and use transformation ducts, to keep the pressure loss to a minimum. Typical values of pressure loss across a splitter are shown in figure 7.30. They can be improved upon by as much as 20 per cent in some cases, by using specially designed nose and

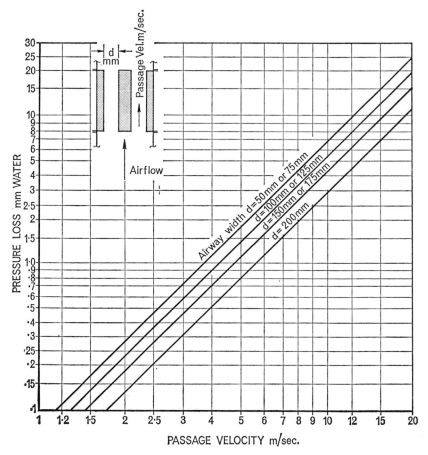

Fig. 7.30. Typical pressure loss in splitter type silencers

tail farings on the splitter elements. Most manufacturers will advise on this.

EXAMPLE 7.3

With the system described in example 5.2, it is written into the specification that the noise level in either of the rooms served, shall not exceed NC35. Select a suitable attenuator for the system.

The room sound pressure levels due to this system were evaluated in example 5.3. The first problem is to evaluate the required insertion loss for a silencer.

Octave Band Centre Freq	Hz	63	125	250	500	1000	2000	4000	8000
SPL in room (example 5.3)	dB	44	49	49	54	57	54	49	43
NC35 (fig. 2.8)	dB	60	52	45	39	36	34	33	32
Required insertion loss	dB	0	0	4	15	21	20	16	9

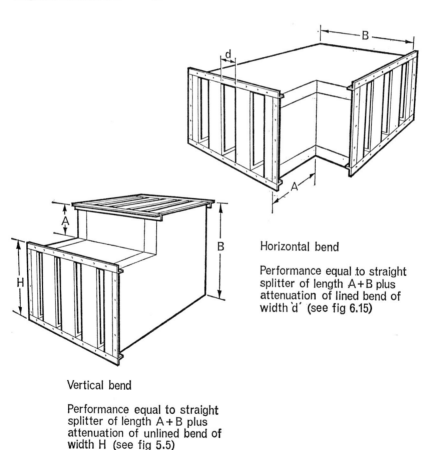

Horizontal bend

Performance equal to straight splitter of length A + B plus attenuation of lined bend of width 'd' (see fig 6.15)

Vertical bend

Performance equal to straight splitter of length A + B plus attenuation of unlined bend of width H (see fig 5.5)

Fig. 7.31. Examples of packaged bend splitter silencers

TABLE 7.2
Attenuation by 200 mm thick sound absorbing splitter modules in a duct

Length mm	Air passage width mm	63	125	250	500	1000	2000	4000	8000
					Attenuation in dB in octave bands Hz				
900	50	8	16	27	45	55	55	55	50
1200	50	10	20	36	55	55	55	55	55
1500	50	13	24	42	55	55	55	55	55
1800	50	15	30	51	55	55	55	55	55
2100	50	17	34	55	55	55	55	55	55
2400	50	19	38	55	55	55	55	55	55
900	75	6	11	19	34	45	45	39	28
1200	75	7	14	26	46	55	55	52	38
1500	75	9	17	30	48	55	55	55	42
1800	75	10	20	34	50	55	55	55	46
2100	75	12	23	40	55	55	55	55	55
2400	75	13	26	45	55	55	55	55	55
900	100	5	9	16	30	39	39	31	26
1200	100	6	12	23	40	51	51	41	29
1500	100	8	15	26	43	53	53	45	32
1800	100	9	17	30	47	55	55	49	36
2100	100	11	20	35	55	55	55	55	43
2400	100	12	23	40	55	55	55	55	47
900	125	4	7	13	25	32	32	23	15
1200	125	5	9	19	33	42	42	30	18
1500	125	7	12	22	38	47	47	34	20
1800	125	8	14	26	43	52	52	39	23
2100	125	9	17	30	50	55	51	46	28
2400	125	10	19	34	55	55	55	52	32
900	150	3	6	11	20	25	25	15	8
1200	150	4	7	15	26	23	33	19	11
1500	150	5	9	18	33	41	41	24	13
1800	150	6	11	22	39	49	49	29	16
2100	150	7	13	26	45	55	55	34	19
2400	150	8	15	29	52	55	55	39	21
900	175	2	5	9	17	21	21	13	5
1200	175	3	6	13	22	28	28	16	7
1500	175	4	8	15	28	35	35	21	8
1800	175	5	9	19	33	42	42	25	9
2100	175	6	11	22	39	49	49	29	11
2400	175	7	13	25	45	55	55	33	11
900	200	1	4	8	15	19	19	11	3
1200	200	2	5	11	20	25	25	14	4
1500	200	3	7	13	25	31	31	18	5
1800	200	4	8	17	29	37	37	22	7
2100	200	5	10	20	34	43	43	25	7
2400	200	6	11	22	39	49	49	29	8

Referring to Table 7.1 we see that this attenuation will be given by a 480 mm diameter circular silencer fitted with a sound absorbing pod. This would be located downstream of the fan bolted either direct to the fan flange, or via a short transformation piece.

Alternatively, a splitter type silencer may be preferred, fixed in the ducting where it emerges from the plant room wall, immediately after the mitre bend. The actual selection would best be carried out by the silencer manufacturer, but we can obtain an idea of the size required by extrapolating from figure 7.29.

With a splitter thickness of 200 mm, a suitable airway would be 175 mm, thus giving a 375 mm module. Two of these would be equal to the duct width of 750 mm. By extrapolation from figure 7.29, we see that an airway of 175 mm and a length of 1200 mm will provide the attenuation required.

Exactly the same remarks apply to bends in the system. As figure 6.15 shows, lining a bend by itself can be most rewarding, but again it is a matter of degree. If very high attenuations are required, it is possible to combine the advantages of a lined bend with those of a splitter silencer as shown in figure 7.31. Again these units can be obtained commercially as a package. Pressure drops tend to be higher in the bend configuration but they can be offset to some extent by using short chord turning vanes.

A variation on the theme of a complete package silencer which is rapidly gaining popularity is the sound absorbing "module". The splitter elements themselves are usually the most difficult to make. Although basically rectangular slabs of the same absorptive material as used for the duct wall lining, the engineering aspects of freely supporting them in the centre of a duct carrying air flow, requires some careful design. It is rather more satisfactory to buy the modules ready made, and self supporting, and then fix them into the available duct on site. They are particularly suitable for builders masonry ducting, and high pressure systems, which require special duct construction. The attenuations that can be obtained by arranging 200 mm thick modules in a duct to give various air passage widths, are shown in Table 7.2.

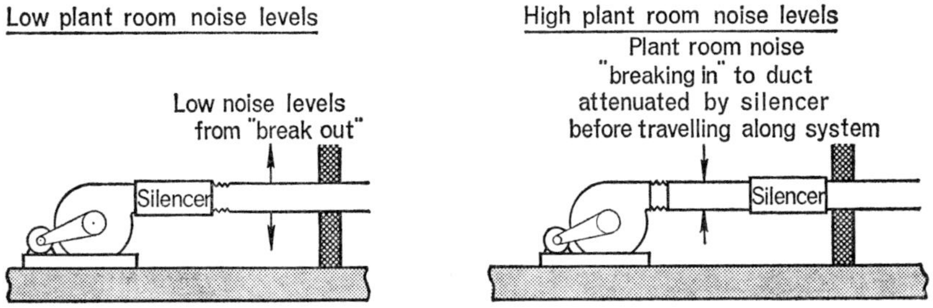

Low plant room noise levels

Low noise levels from "break out"

Silencer

High plant room noise levels

Plant room noise "breaking in" to duct attenuated by silencer before travelling along system

Silencer

Fig. 7.32. Positioning of main silencer in plant room

A duct silencer should always be positioned in the plant room. Exactly where in the plant room depends upon the nature of the equipment there, and its proximity to critical areas. If very low plant room noise is essential, and all the other equipment has been treated, or is already at an acceptable level, then the silencer should be as close to the fan as possible, so that any noise breaking out of the duct into the plant room, will be of relatively low level. This is a general rule to observe in the majority of cases. Where plant room levels are in any case high, it is better to locate the silencer in the duct just before it leaves the plant room. Then, as shown in figure 7.32 any plant room noise entering the system through the duct wall, will be attenuated by the silencer before it can reach the room end of the system.

The advantages of making the walls of a plenum chamber as absorptive as possible, are immediately obvious from equation (5.3). The greater we can make the average absorption in the chamber, the greater will be its room constant, and hence the loss of sound power across the plenum. Note, however that just as in the case of the absorptive treatment of rooms discussed earlier in this chapter, the limiting attenuation in a plenum will be decided by the direct radiation from inlet to outlet. One can improve it further however by fixing a partial baffle across the chamber, which forces the air to travel round its edges, but prevents line of sight, to the outlet. Lining the baffle on both sides also increases the average absorption coefficient.

Control of Secondary Noise

The factors governing secondary noise generation have been listed in Chapter 5. Without doubt the largest single parameter determining the amount of noise generated by a duct element, is the maximum velocity of air past it. The first question is always "can the velocity be reduced?" The sixth power of velocity which almost invariably appears, means that a reduction in velocity of as little as 12 per cent can give a 4 dB decrease in noise.

That being said there will always be a minimum velocity required. If secondary noise is still too high, we must look for some means of attenuating it. The obvious way is to use one or other of the absorptive type attenuators described previously. It is quite common, particularly in high velocity systems, to have a main fan silencer located in the plant room, and secondary silencers (as they are termed), on one or more of the terminal ducts as required. Needless to say, for these to be effective, it is essential that all the secondary noise sources should be positioned far enough back from the terminal unit to give sufficient room for the secondary silencer. This is particularly important with flow control dampers used to adjust the amount of air passing through individual grilles and diffusers. Grille and diffuser noise is virtually untreatable, as the source radiates directly into the occupied space. The same can be said for room induction units. The only control the system designer has is in selection of the quietest available. It is very important then to establish that manufacturers data are actual test results obtained at the particular duty. In an extreme case, the terminal units may have to be oversized.

Indirect and flanking transmission

The control of airborne noise from a plant room to adjacent rooms, has been fully covered earlier in this chapter, in the section on room-to-room control. It is worth drawing attention again however to the possibilities of acoustic louvres where fresh air inlets are required (see fig. 7.18).

EXAMPLE 7.4

The system described in example 5.2 produces the atmospheric side sound pressure levels calculated in example 5.4. If the sound pressure levels outside the apartment window is not to exceed NR 30, propose a suitable method of achieving this.

Octave Band Centre Freq	Hz	63	125	250	500	1000	2000	4000	8000
SPL due to unattenuated fan noise (example 5.4)	dB	37	39	43	43	42	39	34	28
NR 30 (fig. 2.9)	dB	58	48	40	34	30	27	25	23
Attenuation required	dB	0	0	3	9	12	17	9	5

From Table 7.1 we find that this attenuation would be provided by a 300 mm diameter circular silencer fitted with a sound absorbing pod, or any larger size could be selected to bolt directly onto the atmospheric side of the fan.

Alternatively, if there is not sufficient space for a silencer between fan and atmospheric louvre, we could replace the existing louvre with an acoustic louvre. As figure 7.18 shows, this would give ample additional attenuation on the atmospheric side of the system.

Vibration isolation of the fan is essential. The selection of suitable isolators is described in the following section, but there are one or two points which should be emphasised in the context of controlling flanking transmission from fans.

First, if the fan has a separate drive motor, a common bed frame must be provided. If the fan is mounted on its own isolators, and the motor is separately mounted, lateral components of the belt tensions can completely negate the potential of the isolators. Needless to say the selection of the isolators must be based upon the combined weight of fan, drive motor and bed-frame.

The second important point is that a flexible connector between the fan and the discharge and inlet ducting is essential. Moreover, the material from which the connector is made, should have a sound reduction index approaching that of the ducting, which will require a surface density of about 5 to 10 Kg/m². Canvas connectors are too light to prevent noise breakout. Proprietary materials based on high density PVC compounds, which are eminently suitable for this purpose are available, and most fan manufacturers will advise on a suitable grade. When fitting a flexible connector, great care must be taken to ensure it is not "bellowed", for the reason clearly shown in figure 7.28.

One other point that should be made in the context of vibration isolation, is that it is sometimes possible for large ducts to be mechanically excited by a rough airflow inside, even if the fan is completely mechanically isolated from the ducting. It is then necessary to prevent the transmission of the vibration through the building structure, by using resilient hangers. The length of ducting which has to be supported in this way can often be determined by ear, but as a general rule, cylindrical ducts should be supported for about ten diameters. Rectangular ducts should be supported for ten times the maximum duct wall dimensions from the source of the excitation—usually the fan, or a plain elbow.

The factors governing how much "breakout" of noise occurs from a duct crossing a room, were given in equation (5.11). For a given layout, the only parameter we have control over, is the sound reduction index of the duct wall. Practical ways of increasing sound reduction index have been discussed earlier in this chapter, and the same principles apply here.

In the extreme case it may be necessary to completely enclose the duct run over a critical area. Treatment often adequate is to lag the *outside* of the duct with a resilient layer of expanded polyurethane foam, or mineral wool blanket, not less than 50 mm thick, and cover this with a mass skin weighing about 10 Kg/m^2. The principle is to convert the single skin duct to a double skin, hence the mass layer. The purpose of the resilient layer is to provide as much isolation as possible between the two skins. With the 50 mm spacer and 10 Kg/m^2 skin mentioned, an *additional* attenuation through the duct wall of about 7 dB from 63 Hz to 2000 Hz, and 10 dB at 4000 Hz and above, can be expected.

Vibration Isolation

The basic procedure for selecting an isolator is fairly simple. First one decides upon the efficiency of isolation required—one may know the dynamic amplitude of an out-of-balance force for example, and be given a maximum possible dynamic force to be exerted on the structure—the ratio of the two giving the transmissibility. Unfortunately, not all cases are as straightforward and as a general rule one should aim for around 90 per cent efficiency, i.e. 10 per cent transmissibility.

The next thing to decide upon is the lowest forcing frequency likely to be encountered. With rotating machines this is usually the shaft rotational frequency—any electrical exciting forces for example usually being of higher frequency. Reciprocating machinery may have lower frequency components than the shaft frequency, associated with inertia forces or power strokes.

Dealing first with the case where the machine is mounted at ground or basement level, but in any case on a solid foundation, we see from figure 6.18 that if we use an undamped mount, its natural frequency must be about one third of the lowest frequency that we are concerned with. If we have to use a damped mount, its natural frequency must be rather less than this. Fortunately, isolators with damping greater than about 10 per cent of critical damping, are required only in special cases e.g.:

1. Continuously variable speed over a range which includes the natural frequency of the isolator.
2. Machines with long run-up or run-down times.
3. Impact loaded machines.

Once we have decided what the natural frequency should be, that fixes the required static deflection (equation 6.6). In fact, once we have decided that little or no damping is required, we can obtain required static deflection directly in terms of efficiency and lowest forcing frequency from figure 6.19. All we have to do then is to select a stiffness of mount which will give this deflection under its share of the machine weight.

EXAMPLE 7.5

A belt driven fan with an impeller speed of 650 rpm is located in an area where it is imperative that the efficiency of isolation of vibrating forces in the fan and drive motor assembly, shall not be less than 90 per cent. If the rotational speed of the drive motor is 1440 rpm, and the complete assembly weighs 136 Kg, specify the requirements of suitable vibration isolators. The four mounting points on the assembly may be assumed to be equally disposed about the centre of gravity of the assembly.

With four mounting points, the load per mount will be 34 Kg.

We can obtain the required static deflection, knowing the required efficiency is 90 per cent, directly from figure 6.19. The lowest important forcing frequency will be that of the rotational frequency of the fan, i.e. 650/60 = 11 Hz.

Then from figure 6.19, required static deflection = 22·5 mm.

The complete specification of the isolator, will then be

static deflection = 22·5 mm under a load of 34 Kg.

Without doubt it is always best to use a proprietary isolator, and manufacturers will advise on the best unit for the particular application, a fairly straightforward procedure. Often the unit can be selected directly from manufacturers' literature, but there are pitfalls for the unwary, some of the most commonly encountered of which will now be outlined.

Type of Isolator

By far the most common type of anti-vibration mount is the one using rubber-in-shear. Figure 7.33(a) shows typical forms that are readily available commercially Although the selection procedure is as outlined above, the dynamic deflection should be used for calculation because rubber is one of that class of materials whose stiffness increases when actually vibrating. For medium grade rubbers a dynamic deflection about 50 per

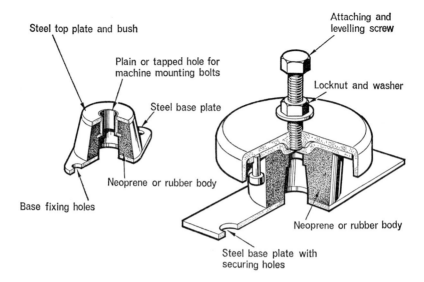

Steel top plate and bush

Attaching and levelling screw

Plain or tapped hole for machine mounting bolts

Locknut and washer

Steel base plate

Neoprene or rubber body

Base fixing holes

Neoprene or rubber body

Steel base plate with securing holes

(a) Rubber or neoprene in shear

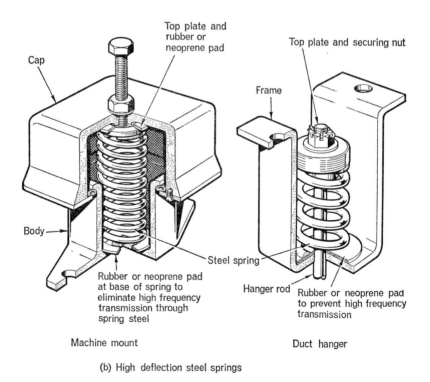

Top plate and rubber or neoprene pad

Top plate and securing nut

Cap

Frame

Body

Steel spring

Rubber or neoprene pad at base of spring to eliminate high frequency transmission through spring steel

Hanger rod

Rubber or neoprene pad to prevent high frequency transmission

Machine mount

Duct hanger

(b) High deflection steel springs

Fig. 7.33. Examples of antivibration mount construction

cent of its static deflection may be assumed. In all cases where proprietary rubber-in-shear mounts are proposed it is best to use manufacturers load-deflection figures, but make sure whether they are static or dynamic deflections.

Rubber-in-shear mounts are generally acceptable for deflection of up to 12·5 mm. For greater static deflection (lower natural frequencies) it will be necessary to use steel spring mounts (fig. 7.33(b)). These have the advantage of preserving linear stiffness and other properties over a wide range of operating conditions, and are generally unaffected by environments like wet or oily conditions. One disadvantage of a steel spring is that high frequency components of the excitation can be transmitted to the foundation by travelling along the coils of the spring itself. For this reason, a spring type isolator should always incorporate a rubber or neoprene pad between the spring and the body of the isolator. Another disadvantage is that the spring by itself has little or no damping. An excellent property as far as efficiency goes, but it does result in very large amplitudes of vibration if the isolator is excited at its natural frequency. If this is likely to occur very often in a particular installation, damping can be added in the form of a mastic compound packed around the spring in the isolator body. There is then of course a consequent loss of efficiency under normal running conditions. In all cases where required static deflections range from about 12·5 mm up to as high as 50 mm, steel springs should be used.

Mats like cork, felt, or proprietary combinations of highly damped elastomers, are not generally satisfactory where good isolation is required over a wide range of frequency. Like rubber, they tend to greater stiffness under dynamic loading and their load deflection curves are not always linear. There is a tendency for some materials to harden with age (thus increasing the natural frequency) and to be attacked by oil or water. Nevertheless they do have their uses, particularly in preventing the higher frequency components like electrical and bearing noises, from being transmitted. As another general rule, they should be restricted to installations where the required static deflection is less than about 6 mm.

Equality of loading

It is absolutely essential that static deflection is equal for each mount on the machine. Failure to ensure this can lead to rocking or pitching motion of the machine—modes of vibration which may have natural frequencies of vibration higher than that of the simple vertical mode. If all the mounts have the same stiffness they must obviously be disposed equally about the centre of gravity of the system. Sometimes extensions to the mounting frame or the addition of an inertia block, is necessary to achieve this as shown in figure 7.34. The alternative is to evaluate exactly the actual load on each mounting point and select mounts of different stiffnesses so that all the individual deflections are equal.

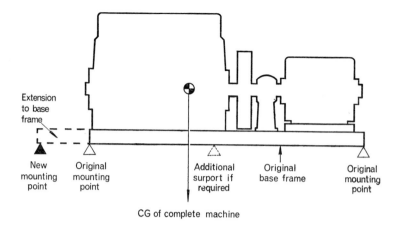

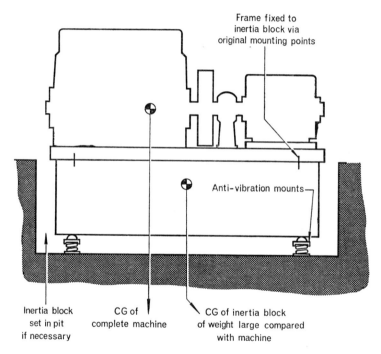

Fig. 7.34. Methods of obtaining equally distributed loads

Flexibility of supporting structure

As we have seen frequently in the course of examining the response of partitions to noise, all structures are flexible to a degree. This is particularly true of floors above grade. If the machine rests directly on the floor, the floor itself acts as a spring, and exhibits exactly the same behaviour as shown in figure 6.18. Now consider what happens if we put a vibration isolator between the machine and the "resilient" floor. We will of course have chosen the natural frequency of the isolator to be well below the lowest frequency likely to be excited strongly by the machine. But the natural frequency of the floor may be below this. The situation is then as summarised in figure 7.35. Even though they are not of very high amplitude, low frequency vibration forces in the machine frame, that is, lower than $\sqrt{2}$ times the natural frequency of the machine mount, will get through to the floor just as if the machine mount were not there. The net result is that the floor is now being excited by forces at frequencies near or at its own resonant frequency. However small these components may be in amplitude it is clearly not a desirable situation.

For installation on high level, or any suspended floor therefore, the natural frequency of the isolator should be at most about half the natural frequency of the floor. In terms of deflection this means the static deflection

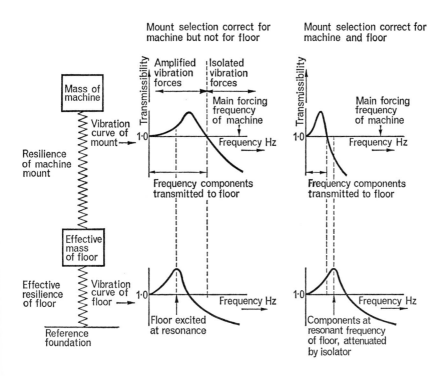

Fig. 7.35. The effect of a resilient foundation on mount selection

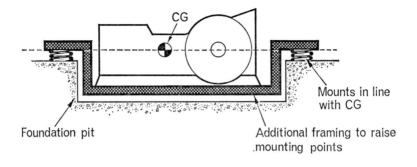

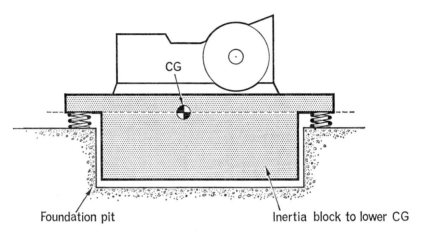

Fig. 7.36. Examples of vertical disposition of mounts

of the isolator under the weight of the machine, should be about three to four times the static deflection of the floor itself under the weight of the machine. The problem comes in trying to estimate what the deflection of the floor will be and this unfortunately is not easy to calculate being dependent upon material, thickness, span and a number of structural parameters. As a rule of thumb, assume a static deflection of about 1/300 of the span.

Lateral Stiffness

A mount which has a lateral stiffness much higher than its vertical stiffness, will have a higher natural frequency with an applied lateral load. The danger then is that if the loading is, for example, like a rotor out-of-balance force, the sideways component could set up a serious lateral resonance. To be safe therefore one should always ensure that the lateral stiffness of an isolator is not greater than the vertical stiffness, and, if possible, rather less.

Allied to this is the problem of vertical disposition of the line of action of horizontal exciting forces on the sprung mass relative to the top of the mount. If it is much higher, there will obviously be an oscillatory couple applied to the system, leading possibly to quite serious pitching motion. The solution as shown in figure 7.36 is to raise the mounts so that the line of action and the top of the mounts are as nearly as possible in the same horizontal plane.

Bridging

Of all the mistakes made in fitting anti-vibration mounts, the most common is mechanical "bridging" of the isolator by some rigid connection between the sprung machine, and the foundation. However carefully the mounts have been selected, they will be valueless if any bridging path is left.

Electrical conduits should be flexibly joined to motor terminal boxes or switchgear, water pipes to pumps, radiators or air handling units should have a length of flexible hose (braided if necessary) immediately before the sprung equipment and air ducts should be connected to the fan by means of a flexible duct connector, as described earlier in the section on ventilation noise control.

The main requirement of flexible connectors of this type is that they should not increase the overall stiffness of the system and hence increase the natural frequency, or add damping and hence lower the efficiency. In practice this is sometimes difficult, particularly where, for example, the connection is to a high pressure water system. Suitable hoses are available commercially however, and the manufacturers will advise on the correct construction and disposition relative to the rigid piping.

APPENDIX A

APPROXIMATE VALUES OF ABSORPTION COEFFICIENT FOR SOME COMMON INTERNAL FINISHES

Material	Thickness (including any airspace) mm	Frequency Hz							
		63	125	250	500	1000	2000	4000	8000
Normal wall finishes									
Brickwork	—	·05	·05	·04	·02	·04	·05	·05	·05
Breeze or cinder block	—	·10	·20	·45	·60	·40	·45	·40	·40
Concrete	—	·01	·01	·01	·02	·02	·02	·03	·03
Up to 4 mm thick glass pane about 1 m square	4	·25	·35	·25	·20	·10	·05	·05	·05
6 mm plate glass about 1m sq.	6	·08	·15	·06	·04	·03	·02	·02	·02
Marble or glazed tile	—	·05	·05	·05	·05	·05	·05	·05	·05
Plaster on solid wall	12	·04	·04	·05	·06	·08	·04	·06	·05
Water (e.g. swimming pool)	—	·01	·01	·01	·01	·01	·02	·02	·02
Wall or ceiling treatments									
Curtains hung in folds against solid wall	—	·05	·05	·15	·35	·40	·50	·50	·40
"Acoustic" plaster (typical values)	12	·05	·10	·15	·20	·25	·30	·35	·35
Sprayed asbestos, direct on wall or ceiling	25	·05	·10	·30	·65	·85	·85	·80	·75
on expanded metal with 75 mm air gap	100	·20	·30	·40	·65	·80	·75	·75	·70
Glass or rockwool blanket typical values for medium density material	25	·05	·10	·35	·60	·70	·75	·80	·75
	50	·10	·20	·45	·65	·75	·80	·80	·80
	100	·25	·45	·75	·80	·85	·85	·90	·85
	150	·35	·55	·90	·90	·85	·90	·95	·95
Expanded polyurethane foam (open cell)	25	·10	·15	·30	·60	·75	·85	·90	·90
	50	·15	·25	·50	·85	·95	·90	·90	·90
	100	·30	·50	·70	·95	1·00	1·00	1·00	1·00
9 mm plasterboard on battens at 0·5 m centres, 18 mm airspace filled with glass wool	27	·30	·40	·35	·20	·15	·05	·05	·05
5 mm plywood on battens at 1 m centres, 50 mm airspace filled with glass wool	55	·25	·30	·20	·15	·10	·05	·05	·05
12 mm plywood on battens at 1 m centres, 59 mm airspace filled with glass wool	71	·25	·30	·20	·15	·10	·10	·10	·05
3 mm hardboard with roofing felt stuck to back over 50 mm airspace	53	·50	·90	·45	·25	·15	·10	·10	·05
Suspended plaster or plasterboard ceiling (large airspace)	—	·20	·20	·15	·10	·05	·05	·05	·05
Fibre board on solid backing	12	·05	·05	·10	·15	·25	·30	·30	·25

APPENDIX A—*continued*

Material	Thickness (including any airspace) mm	Frequency Hz 63	125	250	500	1000	2000	4000	8000
Floor coverings									
Composition flooring	—	·05	·05	·05	·05	·05	·05	·05	·05
Haircord carpet on felt underlay	6	·05	·05	·05	·10	·20	·45	·65	·65
Medium pile carpet on sponge rubber underlay	10	·05	·05	·10	·30	·50	·65	·70	·65
Thick pile carpet on sponge rubber underlay	15	·05	·15	·25	·50	·60	·70	·70	·65
Rubber floor tiles	6	·05	·05	·05	·10	·10	·05	·05	·05
Proprietary acoustic tiles and boards (Note that performance varies according to individual construction and method of fixing. Always obtain exact figures from manufacturer. The figures shown indicate the likely range of performance)									
Fixed direct on wall or ceiling, or with small airspace minimum	12 to 75	·05	·10	·25	·50	·60	·60	·45	·45
maximum	12 to 75	·15	·20	·60	·80	·85	·80	·75	·75
In the form of suspended ceiling minimum	—	·15	·30	·40	·50	·65	·75	·70	·65
maximum	—	·30	·50	·60	·90	·90	·85	·80	·75
Room contents (Figures shown are total value of Sa in m² units)									
Audience per person in fully upholstered seat	—	·15	·20	·40	·45	·45	·50	·45	·40
Audience per person in wood or padded seat	—	·10	·15	·25	·40	·40	·45	·40	·35
Unoccupied seat fully upholstered	—	·05	·10	·20	·30	·30	·30	·35	·30
Unoccupied seat wood or padded	—	·02	·03	·05	·05	·10	·15	·10	·10

o

APPENDIX B

REPRESENTATIVE VALUES OF AIRBORNE SOUND REDUCTION INDEX FOR SOME COMMON STRUCTURES

Partial construction	Thickness mm	Superficial weight kg/m²	Frequency Hz							
			63	125	250	500	1000	2000	4000	8000
Panels of sheet materials										
1·5 mm lead sheet	1·5	17	22	28	32	33	32	32	33	36
3 mm lead sheet	3	34	25	30	31	27	38	44	33	38
20 g aluminium sheet, stiffened	·9	2·5	8	11	10	10	18	23	25	30
22 g galvanised sheet steel	·55	6	3	8	14	20	23	26	27	35
20 g galvanised sheet steel	·9	7	3	8	14	24	26	32	38	40
18 g galvanised sheet steel	1·2	10	8	13	20	27	29	33	39	44
16 g galvanised sheet steel	1·6	13	9	14	21	27	32	37	43	42
18 g fluted steel panels stiffened at edges, joints sealed	1·2	39	25	30	30	22	30	28	31	31
Corrugated asbestos sheet stiffened and sealed	6	10	20	25	20	33	33	38	32	42
Chipboard sheets on wood framework	19	11	14	17	18	25	30	26	31	38
Fibreboard sheets on wood framework	12	4	10	12	16	25	24	30	35	36
Plasterboard sheets on wood framework	9	7	9	15	20	24	29	32	29	38
Plywood sheets on wood framework	6	3·5	6	9	13	16	21	27	35	33
Hardwood (mahogany) panels	50	25	15	19	23	25	30	37	42	46
Woodwork slabs unplastered	25	19	0	0	2	6	6	8	8	10
Woodwool slabs plastered (12 mm on each face)	50	75	18	23	27	30	32	36	39	43
Panels of sandwich construction										
1·5 mm lead between two sheets of 5 mm plywood	11·5	25	19	26	30	34	38	42	44	47
9 mm asbestos board between two sheets of 18 g steel	12	37	16	22	27	31	27	37	44	48
"Stramit" compressed straw between two sheets of 3 mm hardboard	56	25	15	22	23	27	27	35	35	38
Single masonry walls										
Single leaf brick, plastered both sides	125	240	30	36	37	40	46	54	57	59
	255	480	34	41	45	48	56	65	69	72
	360	720	36	44	43	49	57	66	70	72
Solid breeze or clinker blocks, plastered (12 mm both sides)	125	145	20	27	33	40	50	57	56	59
Solid breeze or clinker blocks, unplastered	75	85	12	17	18	20	24	30	38	43
Hollow cinder concrete blocks, painted (cement base paint)	100	75	22	30	34	40	50	50	52	53
Hollow cinder concrete blocks, unpainted	100	75	22	27	32	37	40	41	45	48
"Thermalite" blocks	100	125	20	27	31	39	45	53	38	62
Glass bricks	200	510	25	30	35	40	49	49	43	45
Double masonry walls										
280 mm brick, 56 mm cavity, strip ties, outer faces plastered 12 mm	300	380	28	34	34	40	56	73	76	78
280 mm brick, 56 mm cavity, expanded metal ties, outer faces plastered, 12 mm	300	380	27	27	43	55	66	77	85	85
Stud partitions										
50 mm × 100 mm studs, 12 mm insulating board both sides	125	19	12	16	22	28	38	50	52	55
50 mm × 100 mm studs, 9 mm plaster board and 12 mm plaster coat both sides	142	60	20	25	28	34	47	39	50	56

APPENDIX B—*continued*

Partition construction	Thickness mm	Superficial weight kg/m²	63	125	250	500	1000	2000	4000	8000
							Frequency Hz			
Single glazed windows										
Single glass in heavy frame	6	15	17	11	24	28	32	27	35	39
	8	20	17	18	25	31	32	28	36	39
	9	22·5	18	22	26	31	30	32	39	43
	16	40	20	25	28	33	30	38	45	48
	25	62·5	25	27	31	30	33	43	48	53
Double glazed windows										
2·44 mm panes, 7 mm cavity	12	15	15	22	16	20	29	31	27	30
9 mm glass panes in separate frames, 50 mm cavity	62	34	18	25	29	34	41	45	53	50
6 mm glass panes in separate frames, 100 mm cavity	112	34	20	28	30	38	45	45	53	50
6 mm glass panes in separate frames, 188 mm cavity	200	34	25	30	35	41	48	50	56	56
6 mm glass panes in separate frames, 188 mm cavity with absorbent blanket in reveals	200	34	26	33	39	42	48	50	57	60
6 mm and 9 mm panes in separate frames, 200 mm cavity, absorbent blanket in reveals	215	42	27	36	45	58	59	55	66	70
Doors										
Flush panel, hollow core, normal cracks as usually hung	43	9	9	12	13	14	16	18	24	26
Solid hardwood, normal cracks as usually hung	43	28	13	17	21	26	29	31	34	32
Typical proprietary "acoustic" door, double heavy sheet steel skin, absorbent in airspace, special furniture and seals in heavy steel frame	100	—	37	36	39	44	49	54	57	60
Floors										
T & G boards, joints sealed	21	13	17	21	18	22	24	30	33	63
T & G boards, 12 mm plasterboard ceiling under, with 3 mm plaster skim coat	235	31	15	18	25	37	39	45	45	48
As above with boards "floating" on glass wool mat	240	35	20	25	33	38	45	56	61	64
Concrete, reinforced	100	230	32	37	36	45	52	59	62	63
	200	460	36	42	41	50	57	60	65	70
	300	690	37	40	45	52	59	63	67	72
126 mm reinforced concrete with "floating" screed	190	420	35	38	43	48	54	61	63	67

APPENDIX C
GLOSSARY OF ACOUSTICAL TERMS

ABSORPTION COEFFICIENT If the surface of a material is exposed to a sound field the absorption coefficient of the material is the ratio of the sound energy absorbed by the surface to the total sound energy which strikes it.

ACOUSTICS The science of sound, including its production, transmission, and effects.

AIRBORNE SOUND Sound transmitted through air as a medium rather than through solids or the structure of a building.

AMBIENT NOISE The background noise or prevailing noise in an area, generally in the absence of a noise of particular interest.

ANALYSER, FREQUENCY Electrical apparatus capable of measuring in various frequency bands the acoustic energy present in a complex sound.

ANECHOIC A region or space which is almost totally free of reflection over a wide range of frequencies. An anechoic chamber gives almost free field conditions.

ATTENUATION, SOUND The reduction in intensity of a sound signal.

BACKGROUND LEVEL The normal sound level present in a region above which speech, music or similar wanted sound must be presented.

BAND A segment of the frequency spectrum, i.e. an octave, half octave, third octave.

BEAT Periodic increase and decrease of amplitude resulting from the super-position of two tones of different frequencies f_1 and f_2. The beat frequency is equal to (f_1-f_2).

DAMAGE RISK CRITERION The noise level, as a function of frequency, and factors such as waveform (i.e. pure tone or random) and intermittency, above which permanent hearing loss greater than a specified amount is likely to be sustained by a person subjected to it.

DAMPING Removal of kinetic energy in an oscillating medium by converting it to heat, using frictional or viscous forces.

DECIBEL A division of a uniform scale based upon 10 times the logarithm to the base 10 of the ratio of sound intensities being compared.

DIFFUSE SOUND FIELD A sound field in which the energy density is everywhere the same and sound waves are likely to be travelling in any direction with equal probability.

COINCIDENCE When the length of a bending wave in a panel coincides with the projected length of an incident sound wave striking the panel at some angle. There is a frequency below which coincidence cannot occur and this is called the critical frequency.

FOCUSING Concentration of acoustic energy within a limited location in a room as the result of reflections from concave surfaces.

FREE FIELD A region in which no significant reflections of sound occur (see also ANECHOIC).

FUNDAMENTAL FREQUENCY The frequency with which a periodic function reproduces itself.

HARMONIC A sinusoidal (pure tone) component in a complex periodic wave, of frequency, which is an integral (whole number) multiple of the fundamental frequency of the wave. If a component in a sound has a frequency twice that of the fundamental, it is called the second harmonic.

HEARING LOSS An increase in the threshold of audibility, at specific frequencies, as the result of normal ageing, disease, or injury to the hearing organs.

INTENSITY The rate of sound energy transmitted in a specified direction through a unit area.

LOUDNESS The subjective judgement of the intensity of a sound.

196

MASKING The increase in threshold of audibility of a sound necessary to permit its being heard in the presence of another sound.

NATURAL FREQUENCY The frequency at which a resiliently mounted mass when set into vibration, would vibrate under the influence of gravity alone with no added force or constraints. (Often called "resonant frequency").

NOISE Sound unwanted by the listener, meaningless sound, random sound.

NOISE CRITERIA (NC) A family of octave band spectra giving limiting values of sound pressure level for speech interference and acceptability requirements in particular applications, usually types of office.

NOISE RATING (NR) CURVES OR NUMBERS Similar to NOISE CRITERIA, NR curves apply to a wider range of applications, from factory noise to noise in homes.

OCTAVE The interval between two sounds one of which has a frequency twice that of another.

OCTAVE BAND A range of frequencies whose upper limit is twice the frequency of the lower limit.

PEAK SOUND PRESSURE LEVEL The value in decibels of the maximum sound pressure, as opposed to the root-mean-square, or effective, sound pressure.

PHON A measure of loudness level (on a logarithmic scale) which compares the loudness of a sound to that of a 1,000 cps tone of known sound pressure level.

PLANE WAVES Waves in which the fronts are parallel with one another at right angles to the direction of propagation.

REVERBERATION The persistence of sound within a space after the source has ceased, due to repeated reflection at the boundaries of the space.

REVERBERATION TIME The time it takes for reverberant sound of a given frequency to decay by 60 dB after the source is cut off.

SABIN A measure of sound absorption of a surface. An absorption of 1 sabin is equivalent to 1 square metre of a perfectly absorptive surface.

SOUND POWER LEVEL A value equal to 10 times the logarithm to the base 10 of the ratio of the total acoustic power emitted by a source to a reference power, which is normally taken to be 10^{-12} watt.

SOUND PRESSURE LEVEL A value equal to 20 times the logarithm to the base 10 of the ratio of the root-mean-square pressure of a sound to a reference pressure, which is normally taken to be 2×10^{-5} N/m^2.

SOUND SHADOW The acoustical equivalent to a light shadow, usually partially filled with sound energy as a result of diffraction.

SOUND REDUCTION INDEX 10 times the logarithm to the base 10 of the sound energy incident upon a panel to the sound energy radiated from the opposite side.

SPEECH INTERFERENCE LEVEL The arithmetic average of the sound pressure levels of a sound in the 500 Hz, 1000 Hz and 2000 Hz octave bands.

STRUCTURE BORNE SOUND Sound energy transmitted through solid media such as the building structure.

THRESHOLD OF AUDIBILITY The minimum sound pressure level at which a person can hear a sound of a given frequency.

THRESHOLD OF PAIN OR FEELING The minimum sound pressure level of a sound of given frequency at which a person experiences physical feeling or pain in the ear.

THRESHOLD SHIFT An alteration, either temporary or permanent, in a person's threshold of audibility.

VIBRATION ISOLATION Any of several means of preventing or reducing the transmission of vibrational energy from body to the structure in which or on which it is mounted.

WHITE NOISE Noise of a statistically random nature having equal energy at every frequency over a particular band.

CONVERSION FACTORS

To convert	*Into*	*Multiply by*	*Conversely, multiply by*
Metres	Feet	3·281	0·3048
Millimetres	Inches	0·0394	25·4
Square metres	Square feet	10·8	0·093
Square metres	Square inches	1550	$6·45 \times 10^{-4}$
Cubic metres	Cubic feet	35·31	$2·832 \times 10^{-2}$
Kilograms per square metre	Pounds per square foot	0·204	4·88
Kilograms per cubic metre	Pounds per cubic foot	0·062	16·0
Metres per second	Feet per minute	196·8	$5·08 \times 10^{-3}$
Cubic metres per hour	Cubic feet per minute	0·589	1·7
Kilowatts	Horsepower	1·341	0·746

Bibliography

Text books

Noise Rupert Taylor, Pelican Books 1970.

Teach Yourself Acoustics G. R. Jones, T. I. Hempsted, K. A. Mulholland, M. A. Stott, English Universities Press.

Building acoustics B. F. Day, R. D. Ford, P. Lord, Elsevier 1969.

Acoustics Noise and Buildings P. H. Parkin and H. R. Humphreys, Faber and Faber 1958.

Noise and Man W. Burns, John Murray 1968.

The Control of Noise National Physical Laboratory Symposium No. 12, HMSO 1962.

Noise Reduction L. L. Beranek (Ed), McGraw-Hill 1960.

Acoustics L. L. Beranek, McGraw-Hill 1957.

The Measurement and Suppression of Noise A. J. King, Chapman and Hall 1965.

Fundamentals of Acoustics L. E. Kinsler and A. R. Frey, John Wiley 1966.

Acoustics and Vibration Physics R. W. B. Stephens and A. E. Bate, Edward Arnold 1966.

Vibration and Sound P. M. Morse, McGraw-Hill, 1948.

Works of reference

Noise—Final Report The Committee on the problems of Noise, Cmd 2056, HMSO, 1964.

Handbook of Noise Control C. M. Harris (Ed), McGraw-Hill, 1957.

Handbook of Noise and Vibration Control R. A. Warring, (Ed) Trade and Technical Press, 1970.

ASHRAE Guide and Data Book Systems and Equipment, Chapter 14. American Society of Heating, Refrigeration and Air Conditioning Engineers, 1967.

IHVE Guide Section B.12, Institute of Heating and Ventilating Engineers, 1972 (to be published).

Sound Absorbing Materials E. J. Evans and E. N. Bazely, HMSO, 1964.

The Airborne Sound Insulation of Partitions E. N. Bazely, HMSO, 1966.

Insulation Booklet Lomax Erskine, Published annually.

Acoustics Handbook Hewlett Packard Company, 1969.

Design for Sound Woods of Colchester Ltd, 1970

Acoustical Journals

Noise Control and Vibration Reduction Published quarterly by Trade and Technical Press Ltd., England.

Applied Acoustics Published quarterly by Elsevier Publishing Company Ltd., England.

Technical Review Published quarterly by Bruel and Kjaer, Denmark.

Journal of the Acoustical Society of America Published monthly by the Acoustical Society of America, USA.

Journal of Sound and Vibration Published monthly by Academic Press Ltd., England.

Acoustics Published bi-monthly by Verlaz, West Germany.

British Standards relating to acoustics

BS 661: 1969 Glossary of Acoustical Terms

BS 848: Part 2: 1966 Methods of Testing Fans

BS 2475: 1964 Octave and One-third Octave Band Pass Filters

BS 2750: 1956 Recommendations for Field and Laboratory Measurement of Airborne and Impact Sound Transmission in Buildings

BS 3383: 1961 Normal equal-loudness Contours for Pure Tones and Normal Threshold of Hearing under Free-field Listening Conditions

BS 3489: 1962 Sound Level Meters (Industrial Grade)

BS 3593: 1963 Recommendations on Preferred Frequencies for Acoustical Measurements

BS 3638: 1963 Method for the Measurement of Sound Absorption Coefficients (ISO) in a Reverberation Room

BS 4142: 1967 Method of Rating Industrial Noise Affecting Mixed Residential and Industrial Areas

BS 4196: 1967 Guide to the selection of Methods of Measuring Noise Emitted by Machinery

BS 4197: 1967 A Precision Sound Level Meter

BS 4198: 1967 Method for Calculating Loudness

BS 4718: 1971 Methods of Test for Silencers for Air Distribution Systems

Index